Building Spelling Skills

Book 8

Wer recht beſcheyden wol werden
Der pit got trumbye aufferden
1510

Written and designed by Garry J. Moes
Editors: Michael J. McHugh
Dr. Paul D. Lindstrom

A PUBLICATION OF
Christian Liberty Press

TABLE OF CONTENTS

PREFACE

Dear Teacher or Parent:

Book 8 of the *Building Spelling Skills* series is dedicated to the discovery of roots for the spelling of English words. Understanding the origins of words and word components is often a strong aid in learning and retaining the spelling of English words. Unlike some other, more homogeneous languages, English is a multifaceted tongue which has drawn upon the expressions of numerous other languages. This may account for the richness of our language.

Studying word origins has another benefit. In some modern nations which seem committed to new social, political, economic, and moral orders, deliberate attempts are frequently made to sever citizens from the past by means of language alterations. In some cases, these efforts are wholesale and radical in nature. The godly American wordsmith Noah Webster, in the introduction to his famous 1828 dictionary, explained the rationale for his effort. Among his concerns was preventing innovations in language that tend to cut contemporary readers, writers, and speakers from the meaning of what has been written in the past. Since our heritage is substantially a Christian one, it is imperative that modern students be able to retain an understanding of the historic languages which gave rise to this heritage. This book is intended to serve that purpose.

Exercises are provided which will require, in many cases, considerable dictionary work, since modern word definitions in some ways vary from the literal meanings which the root words had in their source languages. In some cases, elementary definitions are supplied in the lesson; in other cases, students will be required to use a standard dictionary. It is recommended that an unabridged dictionary which contains etymological information be available, although other standard reference dictionaries will suffice. It should be noted that in some of the lessons in which definitions are provided, the meanings given are not always the best or most comprehensive definitions for the words as they are now commonly used. The sometimes cryptic definitions are intended to highlight the most basic denotations as they are derived from etymological roots. This is designed to help the student develop an ability to recognize meanings and spellings, based on word analysis techniques.

In Lesson 2 of each unit, students are asked to demonstrate their vocabulary skills by using specified spelling words in sentences. *Students should be instructed that they may use any form of the list word that best fits the context of their sentence.* Writing sentences also gives students the simple opportunity to again *spell* their list words and to practice correctly spelling other words. Indeed, students are given numerous opportunities to write and rewrite each list word. Extensive practice, in the form of repetitive writing of the selected words, is a major tool in learning to spell English words.

Test pages are provided beginning on page 116 which students should use to write their words for the final test called for in Lesson 5 of each unit.

Various word games and puzzles are included in some units. These are intended to guide the student into carefully recognizing the arrangement of letters and/or syllables in selected list words, an exercise which is important in light of the many irregularities in spelling the words of the English language.

Instructors are encouraged to keep reading and spelling in close fellowship with each other during the teaching process. It is also helpful to keep in mind that there are no shortcuts on the road to developing good spellers. Good spellers are developed by hard work and persistence on the part of both teacher and student.

LEARNING

HOW TO

SPELL WORDS

1. Look at the word. Study every letter.

2. Say the word to yourself.

3. Say it again aloud, and then spell it.

4. Copy the word on paper, naming the letters as you write.

5. Close your spelling book, and test yourself.
   Write the word.
   Do not worry if you do not get it right the first time.

6. Open your spelling book again. Check the word.

7. Study the word one more time, and test yourself
   by writing the word again.

* * * * *

As with all of your school work, always remember to ask God to help you learn and understand what you are doing. Thank Him for His help with every lesson.

U*NIT 1*

physician	atmosphere	pseudonym	physiology
frantic	maniac	symmetry	phenomenon
symptom	orthodox	dialogue	catastrophe
analysis	chronicle	mythology	enthusiastic
athletic	synonym	theology	characteristic

LESSON 1

Study the list words above, using the study plan on page 6.

LESSON 2

Use these list words in sentences.

analysis	phenomenon	frantic
chronicle	atmosphere	theology

LESSON 3

Watch Your Language!

1 Study the meanings of these formulations from the Greek language.

PREFIXES

physi- physio- = nature, natural, relating to the body; from *physis,* Gr., "nature."

syn-, sym- = like, with, together, along with, same; from *syn,* Gr., "with, together, at the same time."

chron- = related to time; from *chronos,* Gr., "time."

orth-, ortho- = exact, correct; from *orthos,* Gr., "straight, right, true."

the-, theo- = God or god; from *theos,* Gr., "God, god."

pseud-, pseudo- = false, fake, abnormal, counterfeit; from *pseudein,* Gr., "to lie, cheat, falsify."

dia-, di- = during, through, two; from *dia,* Gr., "twice."

SUFFIXES

-nym = name; from *onyma,* Gr., "name."

-logy = doctrine, theory, science, study, expression; from *logos,* Gr., "word, reason, speech, account."

2 Write all list words having the combining forms shown above. Circle any of the list words that contain two of these formulations.

_____ _____

_____ _____

_____ _____

_____ _____

_____ _____

_____

3 In a dictionary, find at least one additional word with each of the Greek-based prefixes listed in Exercise 1.

_____ _____

_____ _____

_____ _____

8

Our Living Language

1 Write each of your list words three times on a separate sheet of paper. Review your word list and take a practice test.

2 Study the language history below and be prepared to summarize it from memory.

> Greek is one of the most ancient languages in the world and has had an important influence on our English language. It was in use for centuries before Greek culture began to flourish. People who migrated from Asia settled in the fertile lands of the area now known as Greece. Four dialects, Arcado-Cyprian, Doric, Aeolic, and Ionic, developed in the various areas where these people settled. Each of these dialects contributed to the Greek language of later years. Ionic was the major influence in the development of Attic, a dialect which became the standard form of classical Greek. It was the language of Athens and its surrounding districts. Because of the political power and artistic supremacy of Athens by the 5th century B.C., its language eventually began to dominate the other dialects. Following the conquests of Alexander the Great, educated merchants and emigrants carried the developing Greek language throughout the Greek colonies. Two forms of Greek later emerged, one a pure, literary language and the other a spoken language which was influenced by local languages in use where the Greek (Hellenistic) empire had been extended. Slowly, this common form found its way into some literature, the most notable of which were the Four Gospels of the Bible's New Testament, written in a Greek that was influenced by the language of the Jews. The Romans, who eventually took over the Hellenistic empire and more, used both literary and common Greek; and the language of the Romans, Latin, adopted many Greek words. As the Roman Empire extended into the world, it was taken into ancient Britain, where it eventually influenced the languages which later developed into English.

3 Write all list words ending with '-ic' or '-ac.' In the box, write A or N to indicate which are adjectives or nouns.

☐ _____
☐ _____
☐ _____
☐ _____
☐ _____

LESSON 5

Review your word list and take your final test. Write the words in the spaces provided at the back of this book. Ask God for His help with your test and thank Him for it when you have finished.

4 Unscramble these list words

lissyana _____

phatreesom _____

nonohempen _____

tacaheprots _____

U*NIT 2*

fabricate	lubricate	enumerate	exaggerate
fluctuate	cooperate	emancipate	anticipate
fascinate	punctuate	decapitate	medicate
dissipate	invigorate	discriminate	abrogate
mediate	perpetuate	investigate	impersonate

LESSON 1

Study the list words above, using the study plan on page 6.

LESSON 2

Use these list words in sentences.

enumerate	mediate	fabricate
dissipate	discriminate	abrogate

_____

_____

_____

_____

_____

_____

_____

_____

_____

_____

_____

_____

_____

_____

_____

_____

_____

_____

LESSON 3

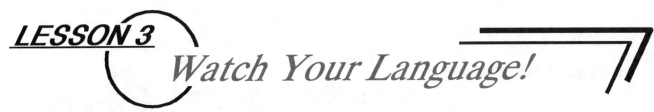

Watch Your Language!

 Study the following information about the suffix '-ate.'

The English suffix '-ate' is derived from the Latin suffix *-atus.* In verbs, the suffix '-ate' means: *(examples in italics)*

1. to act in a specified way *(negotiate, pontificate)*
2. to act upon in a specified way *(assassinate, venerate)*
3. to cause to be modified or affected by *(hyphenate, pollinate)*
4. to cause to become *(activate, domesticate)*
5. to furnish with *(substantiate, capacitate)*

 Write list words that fit the meanings below (save boxes for Exercise 3).

to name or count one by one, to list

to furnish with grease or oil, to apply a lubricant to

to overstate, to represent as greater than actually the case

to set free, to liberate

to abolish or annul by authority, to nullify

to foresee, to act in advance so as to forestall, to expect

to act together toward a common purpose or goal

to distinguish between things, to act prejudicially

to drive away, to scatter, to vanish by dispersion, to lose

to construct by assembling, to make up in order to deceive

to attract intensely, to hold spellbound

to shift irregularly, to waver, to move back and forth

to fill with life or vigor, to impart strength to, to animate

to examine deeply, to make a systematic study of or inquiry into

to assume the character or manner of another person

to help opposing sides reach agreement, to bring about a settlement

to treat with or apply medicine

to cause to be unceasing, to keep a thing lasting forever

to modify written material with standard marks to clarify meaning

to behead, to cut off the head of

In the boxes to the left of each space above, write the number of the definition of the suffix '-ate' (as discussed in Exercise 1) that best fits the list words defined in Exercise 2. Be as precise as you can in analyzing these meanings, even though some answers may be a matter of opinion.

LESSON 4

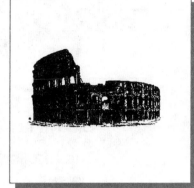

Our Living Language

 Write each of your list words three times on a separate sheet of paper. Review your word list and take a practice test.

 Study the language history below and be prepared to summarize it from memory.

> Latin was the language of the ancient Romans. Although the language is now considered a "dead" language because no groups of people commonly speak it in the modern world, it lives on through its influence on many languages of today. It is most clearly seen in words of the so-called "Romance" languages, a name which comes from the fact that Latin was the language of the "Romans." The Romance (or Roman-influenced) languages of today include: Italian, Spanish, French, Portuguese, and Romanian. Latin became the dominant language of western Europe and much of the rest of the ancient world because the Roman Empire had spread so widely through military conquest. Latin itself developed from several other languages brought to the Italian peninsula by people who spoke Sanskrit, Greek, Germanic, and Celtic tongues. Under the influence of the Greek language and literature, Latin eventually became a great literary language and was used in much of the great poetry and prose of ancient times, from the 3rd century B.C. until as late as the 6th century A.D. Latin remained the language of scholars through the Middle Ages and Renaissance (7th-16th centuries). It lived well into the 20th century as the official language of the Roman Catholic Church, which still uses it in some of its official documents. The study of Latin is useful today, not only for purposes of learning and understanding the important ancient literature of the Romans, but also for understanding those modern languages, including English, which owe so much to Latin.

 Add the suffix '-ion' to make nouns out of your list-word verbs. (Drop final, silent 'e.')

LESSON 5

Review your word list and take your final test. Write the words in the spaces provided at the back of this book. Ask God for His help with your test and thank Him for it when you have finished.

_____ _____

_____ _____

_____ _____

_____ _____

_____ _____

_____ _____

_____ _____

_____ _____

U*NIT 3*

utilize	disparage	encircle	embellish
recognize	intercept	relinquish	manufacture
reconcile	modify	surrender	demoralize
admonish	reprimand	predestine	supersede
accomplish	supplement	preordain	reconnoiter

LESSON 1

Study the list words above, using the study plan on page 6.

LESSON 2

Use these list words in sentences.

disparage	demoralize	supersede
reconnoiter	relinquish	reconcile

Watch Your Language!

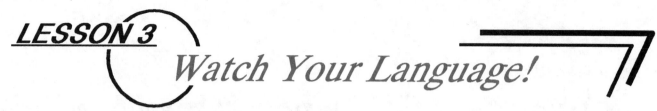

1 The prefix 're-,' from the Latin prefix (re- or red-), means 'again,' 'anew,' or 'back.' Study the 'word trails' below and write the 're-' list words whose roots are being traced.

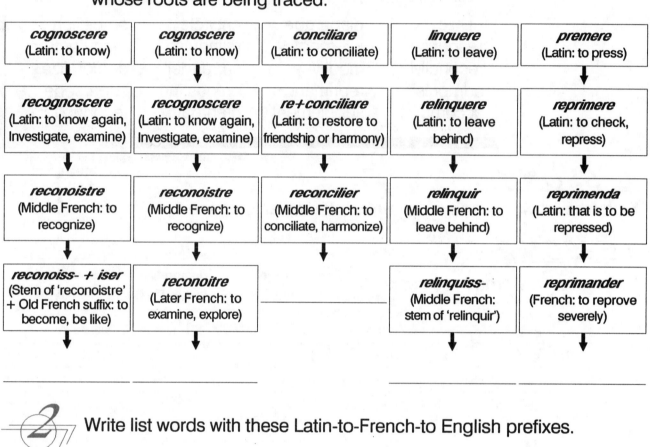

cognoscere (Latin: to know)	*cognoscere* (Latin: to know)	*conciliare* (Latin: to conciliate)	*linquere* (Latin: to leave)	*premere* (Latin: to press)
recognoscere (Latin: to know again, Investigate, examine)	*recognoscere* (Latin: to know again, Investigate, examine)	*re+conciliare* (Latin: to restore to friendship or harmony)	*relinquere* (Latin: to leave behind)	*reprimere* (Latin: to check, repress)
reconoistre (Middle French: to recognize)	*reconoistre* (Middle French: to recognize)	*reconcilier* (Middle French: to conciliate, harmonize)	*relinquir* (Middle French: to leave behind)	*reprimenda* (Latin: that is to be repressed)
reconoiss- + iser (Stem of 'reconoistre' + Old French suffix: to become, be like)	*reconoitre* (Later French: to examine, explore)		*relinquiss-* (Middle French: stem of 'relinquir')	*reprimander* (French: to reprove severely)

_____ _____   _____ _____

2 Write list words with these Latin-to-French-to English prefixes.

ad-, ac-
(to, toward, before) _____

pre-
(before, earlier) _____

dis-, de-
(apart, away, from) _____

en-, em-
(in, within, toward) _____

inter-
(between, among) _____

sup- (sub-)
(up, after, further) _____

sur-, super-
(over, above) _____

England
France
Rome

LESSON 4

Our Living Language

1 Write each of your list words three times on a separate sheet of paper. Review your word list and take a practice test.

2 Study the language history below and be prepared to summarize it from memory.

The earliest inhabitants of Gaul (present-day France) spoke a primitive Celtic language from which Irish, Welsh, and other modern Celtic languages were derived. Celtic gave way in Gaul starting about the 1st century B.C. when the Roman general Julius Caesar conquered that area of Europe and introduced Latin. The form of Latin that took hold in early France was a low form used by the uneducated classes in Rome. By the end of the 4th century A.D., this Latin had replaced Celtic entirely in Gaul. Although a Celtic tongue still is known in the modern French province of Brittany, it was not a survivor of the old Gaulic tongue but was re-introduced by refugees from the British Isles who fled invasions by the Angles, Jutes, and Saxons. Latin became so firmly entrenched in Gaul that later invasions from Germanic tribes, Visigoths, Burgundians, and Franks, did not succeed in imposing their languages. Even today, only about 400 French words have Germanic origins. Some Greek words were introduced into the Roman dialect spoken in Gaul. By the 7th century A.D., the people of France had considerably altered their Romanic (or Romance) language. In the 8th century, the powerful Frankish ruler, Charlemagne, ordered the Church leaders to deliver their sermons in the popular tongue. In medieval times, distinct dialects developed in the north and south. By the 12th century, the northern dialect began to gain supremacy, especially as Paris became the seat of government and the court there exerted power and influence over the other French provinces. This dialect evolved into modern French. French had most of its influence on English following the Norman conquest of England in 1066 A.D. In fact, for a time, French strongly rivaled English as the spoken language of Britain.

3 Write your list words in alphabetical order.

_____   _____
_____   _____
_____   _____
_____   _____
_____   _____
_____   _____
_____   _____
_____   _____
_____   _____

LESSON 5

Review your word list and take your final test. Write the words in the spaces provided at the back of this book. Ask God for His help with your test and thank Him for it when you have finished.

U*NIT 4*

coffee	alcohol	lackey	assassin
mohair	algebra	sultan	zenith
sherbet	chemistry	harem	arabesque
amulet	talisman	monsoon	masquerade
alkali	artichoke	elixir	magazine

LESSON 1

Study the list words above, using the study plan on page 6.

LESSON 2

Use these list words in sentences.

talisman	lackey	masquerade
amulet	assassin	mohair

_____

_____

_____

_____

_____

_____

_____

_____

_____

_____

_____

_____

_____

_____

_____

_____

_____

_____

LESSON 3

Watch Your Language!

1 Fill in the blanks with list words.

1. Tea is to _____ as liquor is to _____.

2. Dessert is to _____ as mathematics is to _____.

3. Newspaper is to _____ as cauliflower is to _____.

4. Salt is to _____ as _____ is to wool.

5. Rain is to _____ as tonic is to _____.

6. King is to queens as _____ is to _____.

7. Magic is to occult as _____ is to _____.

8. Murderer is to _____ as slave is to _____.

9. Chemical is to _____ as apex is to _____.

10. Mask is to _____ as _____ is to design.

2

Write: **assassin** _____

The word "assassin" has an interesting history. The word originates from the Arabic word "hashshashin," plural of "hashshash," meaning one who smokes or chews hashish. Hashish is an narcotic drug similar to marijuana, both of which come from hemp. The "Hashshashin" were members of a secret order of Muslims who terrorized Christians during the period of the Crusades. Their terrors included secret murders committed while they were under the influence of hashish. The name Hashshashin eventually was incorporated into medieval Latin in the word "assassinus," meaning a murderer, especially one who murders for hire or under fanatic devotion to some cause. This is now the essential meaning of the modern English word assassin.

Can you identify these victims of assassins?

Choose: John F. Kennedy
Abraham Lincoln
Martin Luther King, Jr.

_____   _____   _____

3

a _ a _ e _ _ _ _ e	_ _ i _ i _	_ a _ _ _ _ _ a _
_ l _ o _ ol	_ a _ a _ _ _ _	_ o _ _ oo _
_ ss _ ss _ _ _	_ _ e _ _ e _	_ a _ _ _ _ e _ a _ e
a _ _ _ _ _ _ a	_ _ ff _ _ _	al _ al _

Complete these list words. >>>

17

Our Living Language

1 Write each of your list words three times on a separate sheet of paper. Review your word list and take a practice test.

2 Study the language history below and be prepared to summarize it from memory.

Arabic is one of the languages in the Semitic family of languages. Some form of Arabic has been in continual use for about 3,000 years. It is chiefly spoken and written in Arabia, its birthplace, and in other Arab countries of the Middle East and North Africa. The earliest form of the language was known as South Arabic, and inscriptions dated as far back as 800 B.C. have been found. The other form of the language is known as North Arabic and is largely the form in use today. The Arabic "alphabet" is a complicated type of script which is also employed in Persian, Urdu, and older forms of Turkish writing. Arabic retains some ancient forms of grammar and phonetics which have disappeared from other Semitic languages. Modern literary Arabic has been simplified somewhat in style and vocabulary. Common, spoken Arabic varies considerably from country to country in pronunciation and grammar. Thus it is sometimes difficult for common people from these various countries to understand one another. The best known piece of literature written in Arabic is the Koran, the holy book of the Muslim religion, Islam.

3 Write these words. Find them in a dictionary and learn their meanings.

alkali	lackey
amulet	masquerade
arabesque	monsoon
artichoke	talisman
elixir	zenith

Arabesque

LESSON 5

Review your word list and take your final test. Write the words in the spaces provided at the back of this book. Ask God for His help with your studies and test.

UNIT 5

glen	drudgery	flannel	bicker
brag	knickknack	knuckle	slogan
clan	dagger	shamrock	docket
skein	cradle	griddle	maggot
quaff	shanty	harness	ribbon

LESSON 1

Study the list words above, using the study plan on page 6.

LESSON 2

Use these list words in sentences.

clan	drudgery	knuckle
bicker	slogan	harness

_____

_____

_____

_____

_____

_____

_____

_____

_____

_____

_____

_____

_____

_____

_____

_____

_____

Watch Your Language!

1 Write list words in which you hear these consonant sounds.

A. 'N' spelled 'kn,' 'n,' or 'nn' _____ _____

_____ _____ _____

_____ _____ _____

B. 'K' spelled 'c,' 'q,' 'k,' or 'ck' _____

_____ _____ _____

_____ _____ _____

C. 'L' spelled 'l,' 'le,' or 'el'

_____ _____ _____

_____ _____ _____

D. 'B' spelled 'b' or 'bb'

_____ _____ _____

E. 'G' (as in go) spelled 'g' or 'gg'

Name this
picture with
a list word.

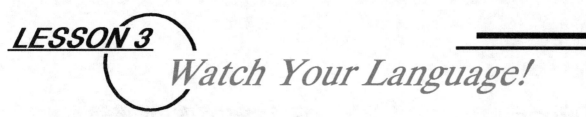

_____ _____ _____

_____ _____ _____

F. 'J' spelled 'g' _____ _____

2 Write list words that are synonyms for the words below.

worm _____ shack _____ knife _____

motto _____ drink _____ boast _____

quarrel _____ valley _____ calendar _____

LESSON 4

· · · · · · · · · · · · · · · · · ·

Our Living Language

1 Write each of your list words three times on a separate sheet of paper. Review your word list and take a practice test.

2 Study the language history below and be prepared to summarize it from memory.

The Celts were a group of people who first appeared in Europe about 2,000 years B.C. and eventually became the dominant force in north-central Europe. The most important of the 150 Celtic tribes were the Britons and Gauls (or Goidels). They moved into the islands west of Europe, now known as Ireland, the Isle of Man, and parts of Great Britain (Scotland, Wales, Northern Ireland, and England). The Goidels (Gauls) spoke a language that became known as Gaelic. Versions of Gaelic are still spoken in Ireland, Scotland, and the Isle of Man (Manx). Other Celtic languages include Welsh (spoken in Wales), Cornish (spoken in the Cornwall area of England), and Breton (spoken in Brittany, a region of western France), all from the Brythonic branch of the Celtic languages. The Celts had well-developed customs, religion, and strong central governments. Their religion was deeply pagan, filled with magical ceremonies, demons, and elves, including the mischievous leprechauns of popular Irish mythology. A mysterious order of pagan priests, known as the Druids, performed rituals involving demons and sun gods. It is believed they may have practiced some of these rituals at a temple known as Stonehenge, whose ruins still stand on the Salisbury Plains of England (see picture above). The Celts had strong tribal or clan divisions, which still survive in the clan structure of Scotland. The ancient Celts had no literature, but passed on their ideas orally. The stories and poetry of the Celts were often told by singers and minstrels who chanted tribal traditions, sang patriotic songs, and told folk tales. Celtic music and tales are popular today in many cultures.

3 Write these words. Find them in a dictionary and learn their meanings.

Use all of these letters in forming two list words.

kkkkkknnnccciaule

_____

_____

skein   shamrock

_____ _____

knickknack   knuckle

_____ _____

flannel   quaff

_____ _____

griddle   bicker

_____ _____

drudgery   docket

LESSON 5

Review your word list and take your final test. Write the words in the spaces provided at the back of this book. Ask God for His help with your studies and test.

UNIT 6

boor	bluff	caboose	wainscot
plug	frolic	loiter	yawl
swab	ballast	holster	brandy
yacht	trigger	easel	clinker
sloop	skipper	morass	beleaguer

LESSON 1

Study the list words above, using the study plan on page 6.

LESSON 2

Use these list words in sentences.

frolic	loiter	holster
easel	trigger	boor

Watch Your Language!

1 Write these nautical list words that show the Dutch are a seafaring people. Put a check mark (✔) in the box beside words that name types of boats.

yacht ☐ _____

sloop ☐ _____

yawl ☐ _____

ballast ☐ _____

skipper ☐ _____

swab ☐ _____

2 Write English words from your word list which were derived from these old Dutch words.

_____ *zwabben (to sway); swabbe (a mop)*

_____ *schipper (a boatman)*

_____ *clinken (a brick)*

_____ *ezel (donkey, ass)*

_____ *wagenschot (a wooden partition)*

_____ *holster (a cover)*

_____ *moeras, moer (mire, swamp)*

_____ *leuteren (to dawdle)*

_____ *jacht (light sailing vessel)*

_____ *belegeren (be+leger [camp])*

_____ *boer (farmer, peasant)*

_____ *vroolijk (joyfully)*

_____ *blaf (flat, broad)*

_____ *kabuis, kombuis (a cookhouse on a deck or ship)*

LESSON 4

· ·

Our Living Language

1 Write each of your list words three times a separate sheet of paper. Review your word list and take a practice test.

2 Study the language history below and be prepared to summarize it from memory.

Dutch is the language of The Netherlands, the northern part of Belgium, a northern area of France, and several overseas territories or former territories of The Netherlands. It is a member of the western group of the Germanic branch of Indo-European languages. Another language that is identical to "high" Dutch is Afrikaans or Cape Dutch, spoken in South Africa, which was settled by Dutch "boers." The Bible and a book of musical versions of the Psalms, The Psalter, have played an important role in the development of the Dutch language, which may be divided into three main periods. Old Dutch, which was in use until about A.D. 1100, was the language of the original Dutch Psalter, copies of which still survive. It developed from the dialects of Flanders, Brabant, and Holland, during the periods these areas were dominant in politics and economics. Middle Dutch was a development of the language from about 1100 until 1550. During the early part of this period, no standard form of Dutch was created for literary purposes, but in the 13th century efforts were made to establish a standard written form of the language. However, the use of common dialects, *Dietsch* continued to prevail. Modern Dutch extends from 1550 to the present day. The greatest event in the history of the language during this period was the publication of the "Statenbijbel," the officially authorized version of the Bible. The form of the language used in this translation of the Bible did much to spread standard modern Dutch throughout the Low Countries. Modern Dutch and Flemish are almost identical.

3 Unscramble these list words. ➡

osobeca _____

chaty _____

waly _____

rinckle _____

lasee _____

agluberee _____

clifor _____

saroms _____

darnby _____

slablat _____

griterg _____

treshlo _____

LESSON 5

Review your word list and take your final test. Write the words in the spaces provided at the back of this book. Ask God for His help with your studies and test.

24

UNIT 7

ardent	fervent	emergent	impenitent
frequent	inclement	dissonant	benevolent
dormant	transparent	impatient	irreverent
flagrant	abstinent	indifferent	irrelevant
poignant	repugnant	impertinent	exorbitant

LESSON 1

Study the list words above, using the study plan on page 6.

LESSON 2

Use these list words in sentences.

impatient	benevolent	repugnant
transparent	fervent	frequent

Watch Your Language!

1 In English adjectives, the suffix '-ant' means 'performing (a specified action)' or 'being (in a specified condition).' The suffix '-ent' has a very similar meaning: 'doing, behaving, or existing (in the specified way).' Write your list words in the appropriate column, according to the suffix.

-ant

-ent

_____

_____

_____

_____

_____

_____

2 In English adjectives, the prefixes 'in-,' 'im-,' and 'ir-' mean 'not.' Write list words with these prefixes in the appropriate columns.

in-   **im-**   **ir-**

_____   _____   _____

_____   _____   _____

_____

LESSON 4

·····················

Our Living Language

1 Write each of your list words three times on a separate sheet of paper. Review your word list and take a practice test.

2 Do the following exercises.

A. Review the language history on page 15.

B. Look up the two words below in a dictionary and write brief definitions showing how they are similar or different in meaning.

| *ardent* | _____ |

_____

| *fervent* | _____ |

_____

C. Write: *poignant.* _____ Look this word up in a dictionary and learn to pronounce it properly. Which letter is silent? How is the first 'n' pronounced? (State your answers orally to your teacher, parent, or classroom helper.)

D. The Latin word 'bene' means 'well.' The Latin word 'volens' means 'willing' or 'wishing.' Based on these facts, what do you think the list word 'benevolent' means? Check your answer in a dictionary.

Write: *benevolent.* _____

LESSON 5

Review your word list and take your final test. Write the words in the spaces provided at the back of this book. Ask God for His help with your studies and test.

3 Change the final 't' to 'ce' in rewriting these list words.

impenitent _____   irrelevant _____

impatient _____   exorbitant _____

abstinent _____   frequent _____

irreverent _____   benevolent _____

indifferent _____   impertinent _____

dissonant _____   emergent _____

UNIT 8

noxious	sumptuous	fastidious	licentious
impious	frivolous	impervious	voluptuous
amorous	judicious	ambiguous	obsequious
arduous	stupendous	gratuitous	insidious
ludicrous	contiguous	discourteous	propitious

LESSON 1

Study the list words above, using the study plan on page 6.

LESSON 2

Use these list words in sentences.

frivolous	discourteous	impious
ambiguous	ludicrous	sumptuous

_____
_____
_____
_____
_____
_____
_____
_____
_____
_____
_____
_____
_____
_____
_____
_____

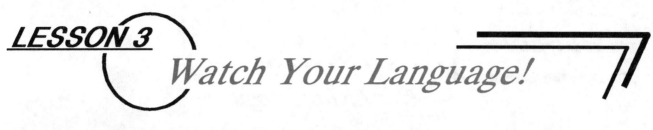

Watch Your Language!

1. In English adjectives, the suffix '-ous' means 'having, full of, abounding in, possessing the qualities of.' Study these Latin root words and their meanings. Write the list word derived from them and a brief definition of the list word.

_____ 'ambiguus'; from 'ambigere' (to wander about, waver, dispute)

_____ 'amorosus'; from 'amor' (love); from 'amare' (to love)

_____ 'arduus' (high, steep, difficult); from 'ardere' (to burn)

_____ 'contiguus;' from 'contigere' (to touch on all sides)

_____ 'dis-' (apart) + 'cohors' (court); fr. 'co-' (with) + 'hortus' (garden)

_____ 'fastidiosus' (haughty); from 'fastus' (pride) + 'taedium' (disgust)

_____ 'frivolus'; probably from 'friare' (to rub, to crumble)

_____ 'gratuitus'; from 'gratus' (pleasing, grateful); from 'gratia' (favor, grace)

_____ 'impervius'; from 'in' (not) + 'per' (through) + 'vius' or 'via' (way, road)

_____ 'impius'; fr. 'in' (not) + 'pius' (pious); fr. 'piare' (appease), 'purus' (pure)

_____ 'insidiosus' (cunning, deceitful); from 'insidiae' (ambush)

_____ 'judicium' (judgment)

_____ 'licentiosus'; from 'licentiare' (to allow); from 'licentia' (license)

_____ 'ludicrus'; from 'ludere' (to play)

_____ 'noxius'; from 'noxa' (damage); from 'nocere' (to harm)

_____ 'obsequiosus'; fr. 'obsequi' (to yield); from 'ob-' (toward) + 'sequi' (follow)

_____ 'propitius'; from 'pro-' (before) + 'pitius,' akin to 'petere' (to go to, seek)

_____ 'stupendus'; from 'stupere' (to be astonished)

_____ 'sumptuosus'; from 'sumptus' (cost, expense)

_____ 'volupuosus'; from 'voluptas' (pleasure, delight)

Our Living Language

 Write each of your list words three times on a separate sheet of paper. Review your word list and take a practice test.

 Write your list words again below, grouping them according to the spelling of their endings.

? + i + ous

_____

_____

_____

_____

_____

_____

_____

_____

? + u + ous

_____

_____

_____

_____

? + ous

_____

_____

_____

_____

_____

? + e + ous

_____

 Add the correct ending to these list words.

LESSON 5

Review your word list and take your final test. Write the words in the spaces provided at the back of this book. Ask God for His help with your studies and test.

nox_____   sumpt_____   fastid_____   licent_____

imp_____   frivol_____   imperv_____   volupt_____

amor_____   jud_____   ambig_____   obsequ_____

ard_____   stupend_____   gratuit_____   insid_____

ludicr_____   contig_____   discourt_____   propit_____

30

U*NIT 9*

vacuum	advocacy	vernacular	benefit
bachelor	equestrian	recognition	reminisce
condiment	destination	contradiction	regalia
pendulum	indignation	centennial	velocity
dimension	propensity	ventriloquist	oblivion

LESSON 1

Study the list words above, using the study plan on page 6.

LESSON 2

Use these list words in sentences.

benefit	**oblivion**	**bachelor**
destination	**velocity**	**regalia**

LESSON 3

Watch Your Language!

1. Fill in the blanks with list words (or plurals of list words).

1. The death of my grandmother left a _____ in my grandfather's life.

2. Senator Thorp was well-known for his _____ of protection for the unborn.

3. "What shall I render unto the Lord for all his _____ to me?" (Psalm 116:12, KJV).

4. My uncle has never been married, but he says he enjoys the life of a _____ .

5. The ship left Seattle today but was not expected to reach its final _____, Tokyo, for three weeks.

6. My father likes to _____ about his boyhood days on the farm.

7. Next year our town will be 100 years old, and a large _____ celebration is planned.

8. The queen wore her velvet cape, her jewels, her crown, and other _____ .

9. In a hurricane, the wind _____ may exceed 100 miles per hour.

10. My sister seems to have a _____ for talking long hours on the telephone.

11. The City Council gave Mr. Taylor a special award in _____ of his many years of community service.

12. Since few people could read Latin, the language of scholars, the Bible was translated in the _____ .

13. Edgar Bergen was a famous _____ many years ago, and his "dummy" was Charlie McCarthy.

14. Mrs. Boswick expressed great _____ over the insults which had been leveled against her singing voice.

15. The Spanish Riding School of Vienna, with its great white stallions, is a world-famous _____ center.

16. The _____ of the old schoolhouse clock swayed slowly as a loud "tick-tock" echoed through the room.

17. Some critics say that the phrase "Christian Rock Music" is a _____ in terms.

18. The hamburgers are on the grill, and the mustard, onions, and other _____ are on the table.

19. Six feet by 10 feet by 8 feet were the _____ of the playhouse my father built for my sister and me.

20. As George grew into very old age, his bitter memories of the war gradually faded into _____ .

2. Write all list words with the suffix '-ion.'

_____ _____ _____

_____ _____ _____

32

Our Living Language

 Write each of your list words three times on a separate sheet of paper. Review your word list and take a practice test.

 WORD ASSOCIATION. Combine words from Group A with appropriate words from Group B.

A

vacuum
bachelor
ketchup
clock
shape
advocacy
horses
travel
anger
talent
language
perception
opposite
anniversary
ventriloquist
advantage
reminisce
royalty
bullet
oblivion

_____ : _____
_____ : _____
_____ : _____
_____ : _____
_____ : _____
_____ : _____
_____ : _____
_____ : _____
_____ : _____
_____ : _____
_____ : _____
_____ : _____
_____ : _____
_____ : _____
_____ : _____
_____ : _____
_____ : _____
_____ : _____
_____ : _____
_____ : _____

B

vernacular
recognition
contradiction
centennial
voice
forgetfulness
velocity
regalia
memories
benefit
cleaner
dimension
single
pendulum
condiment
destination
equestrian
indignation
representation
propensity

LESSON 5   Review your word list and take your final test. Write the words in the spaces provided at the back of this book. Ask God for His help with your studies and your test.

UNIT 10

adamant	prolific	prototype	lethargy
antidote	rhapsody	economize	archetype
parable	scorpion	alabaster	architecture
heresy	pantomime	hypocrisy	pedagogue
galaxy	anonymous	topography	archive

LESSON 1

Study the list words above, using the study plan on page 6.

LESSON 2

Use these list words in sentences.

parable	heresy	economize
hypocrisy	prototype	adamant

LESSON 3

Watch Your Language!

1 Write these four words. In the boxes, write the number of the correct pronunciation of the 'ch' in each word.

☐ **arch** _____

☐ **archetype** _____

☐ **architecture** _____

☐ **archive** _____

PRONUNCIATIONS OF 'CH'
1. 'tch' as in 'church'
2. 'k' as in 'choir'
3. 'sh' as in 'chivalry'

2 The word 'arch,' meaning 'a structure with a curved top,' is of Middle English origins. The prefixes 'arche-' and 'archi-' in the three list words words above are of French, Latin, and Greek origins. The fundamental root is the Greek 'arche,' meaning 'beginning, origin, government.' Study the word analyses below. Then write a brief English dictionary definition of each word in the blank provided.

{ *arche + typos* (image, model, type) = ***archetypos*** *(molded first as a model)*
archetype _____

{ *arche + tekton* (workman, carpenter) = ***architekton*** *(master builder)*
architecture _____

{ *archeion* (government house); ***plural:*** *archeia* (archives)
archive _____

_____

3 Write: **prototype.** _____ (Greek: *protos,* akin to *pro,* meaning 'before' + *typos,* meaning 'type, model.')

(Compare with **archetype.**)

Write a definition of **prototype.** _____

_____

35

Our Living Language

 Write each of your list words three times on a separate sheet of paper. Review your word list and take a practice test.

 Identify these pictures with list words.

 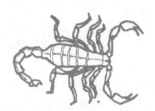  

_____ _____ _____ _____

 Read these Bible passages (King James Version). Which list word do you associate with each one?

Matthew 13:3 _____   Matthew 23:28 _____

Matthew 26:7 _____   2 Timothy 4:3-4 _____

4 Write list words that are synonyms for these words.

teacher _____		**laziness** _____
immovable _____		**unidentified** _____
cure _____		**conserve** _____
fruitful _____		**ecstasy** _____

LESSON 5   Review your word list and take your final test. Write the words in the spaces provided at the back of this book. Ask God for His help with your studies and your test.

UNIT 11

feasible	delectable	amenable	combustible
immutable	compatible	invulnerable	fusible
illegible	impregnable	irrepressible	intractable
infallible	ineligible	portable	applicable
improbable	insensible	reclaimable	irretrievable

LESSON 1

Study the list words above, using the study plan on page 6.

LESSON 2

Use these list words in sentences.

illegible	ineligible	feasible
portable	delectable	infallible

LESSON 3

Watch Your Language!

1

A. What is the meaning of the suffixes '-able' and '-ible' used in the list words for this unit? Consult a dictionary, if necessary.

_____

B. What is the meaning of the prefix 'in-' used in the list words for this unit? Consult a dictionary, if necessary.

_____

C. What forms does the prefix mentioned in B take in list words for this unit? Write the list words with these prefixes in the correct columns. (You will not need to fill all of the lines in all of the columns.)

____	____	____	____
____	____	____	____
____	____	____	____
____	____	____	____
____	____	____	____
____	____	____	____

2 Write the list words whose Latin and French roots are shown below.

(L) admener (to lead to) (F) amener (to bring) + able	(L) fusibilis (able to melt) (F) fusible (able to be fused)	(L) comburere (to burn) (F) combustible (capable of burning)
_____	_____	_____

(L) applicare (to attach) (F) appliquer (to apply) + able	(L) compati (to have compassion) (F) compatible (compassionate)	(L) portare (to carry) (F) portable (able to be carried)
_____	_____	_____

(L) facere (to do) (F) fais-, fr. faire (to do) + ible	(L) delectare (to delight) (F) delectable (delightful)	(L) reclamare (to call for) (F) reclamer (to appeal to) + able
_____	_____	_____

. . . .

Our Living Language

1 Write each of your list words three times on a separate sheet of paper. Review your word list and take a practice test.

2 Write your list words in the correct column, according to the spelling of the suffix.

-able

_____
_____
_____
_____
_____
_____
_____
_____
_____

-ible

_____
_____
_____
_____
_____
_____
_____
_____

3 The Latin word 'mutare' means 'to change.' From this, we get the English words 'mutant,' 'mutation,' 'commute,' and others. Read Malachi 3:6 in the Bible. Which list word is a description of one of God's attributes, according to this verse?

_____

LESSON 5

Review your word list and take your final test. Write the words in the spaces provided at the back of this book. Begin the test with prayer and thank God for His help at the end.

UNIT 12

Words in regular type below are from Hebrew. Words in slanted type are from Persian.

seraph	mammon	hosanna	*paradise*
cherub	sabbath	cinnamon	*caravan*
manna	sapphire	leviathan	*jasmine*
amen	jubilee	hallelujah	*gypsum*
hyssop	Pharisee	*ghoul*	*peach*

LESSON 1

Study the list words above, using the study plan on page 6.

LESSON 2

Use these list words in sentences.

paradise	caravan	peach
cherub	sabbath	ghoul

_____

_____

_____

_____

_____

_____

_____

_____

_____

_____

_____

_____

_____

_____

_____

_____

_____

_____

_____

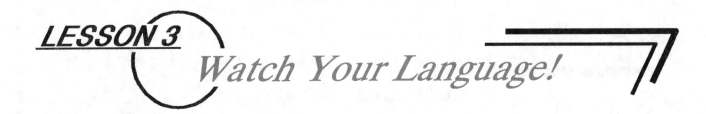

Watch Your Language!

 Read the following verses from the Bible (KJV). Write the list word you find in each verse.

Exodus 16:15 _____

Exodus 20:8 _____

Exodus 30:23 _____

Psalm 51:7 _____

Matthew 6:24 _____

Ezekiel 1:26 _____

Leviticus 25:12 _____

Acts 26:4-5 _____

Isaiah 27:1 _____

Mark 11:9 _____

I Chronicles 16:36 _____

Psalm 18:10 _____

ANGELS

In His work of creation, God made not only the visible world, but also some spiritual or heavenly beings known as angels. The Bible speaks of at least two types of angels. One is a 'cherub,' the other a 'seraph.' In the Bible, the plural of these two words is 'cherubim' and 'seraphim.' The King James Version of the Bible spells the plurals with an ending '-s,' (cherubims, seraphims). In English literature outside of the Bible, the plurals are: 'cherubs' and 'seraphs.' In the Bible, cherubim are described as God's messengers who assist, deliver, and protect God's people. They are described as heavenly creatures who may appear in human or animal form with faces of a lion, ox, man, or eagle. Seraphim means 'burning ones.' The prophet Isaiah saw them standing before the throne of God.

Write these words:

cherub_____

cherubim_____

seraph_____

seraphim_____

PRAISE WORDS

Wherever the God of the Bible has become known, three words from the Hebrew language have found their way into the other languages of the world, in some form or another. These words are: 'amen,' 'hallelujah,' and 'hosanna.' All three are words of worship, spoken to God.

Amen means 'confirm' or 'support.' In English usage, it means 'So let it be,' 'truly,' or 'indeed.'

Hallelujah is Hebrew for 'Praise the Lord.' Hallelu Yah. Yah is a short form of Yahweh, the name of God which is translated in English 'Jehovah' or 'The LORD.'

Hosanna is Hebrew for 'save now.' It became a prayer in itself: 'Save, now, pray.' It was chanted when Jesus rode into Jerusalem to indicate the coming of His Kingdom.

Write these words:

amen _____

hallelujah _____

hosanna _____

NOTE: Hallelujah is sometimes spelled Alleluia.

Our Living Language

 Write each of your list words three times on a separate sheet of paper. Review your word list and take a practice test.

 Study the language histories below and be prepared to summarize them from memory.

Hebrew is a Semitic language. The word 'Semitic' comes from the name of Shem, one of the sons of Noah, from whom the Jews (Hebrews) are descended. It was the language adopted by the Israelites after they took possession of the land of Canaan. Modern Hebrew is the official language of the nation of Israel. Biblical Hebrew, an ancient form of the language, is the language of the Hebrew Bible and the Old Testament of the Christian Bible, both of which are in use today. Biblical Hebrew dates back to the 12th century B.C. and was a 'living' language until about the 2nd century B.C. It is believed that in its earliest forms, Hebrew was similar or identical to Phoenician. Hebrew is considered more important than Phoencian, probably because of the wealth and richness of the Hebrew literature, most of which is religious. After 586 B.C., when the remaining portion of ancient Israel known as Judah was conquered by Babylon, the Jews in Palestine began to use Aramaic in both speech and secular writings. Jews outside Palestine spoke the languages of the countries where they lived. Hebrew was preserved, however, as the language of the rituals of Judaism and the sacred writings of the Jewish people. The modern Hebrew alphabet consists of 22 characters. The vocabulary of modern Hebrew is taken from Biblical Hebrew; the syntax follows that of the Mishnah, the ancient work containing the religious laws established by the Hebrew rabbis. When ancient Hebrew was resurrected as the modern language of Israel in 1948, new words were needed to express scientific and other modern concepts. A Lithuanian-born Jewish scholar, Elieser Ben-Yahuda, invented some 4,000 new terms from Biblical Hebrew roots to meet this need. The various national languages of Jewish immigrants, and Yiddish, the language of eastern European Jews, have also influenced modern Hebrew.

Persian is the language of the modern country of Iran. It is a member of the Iranian family of languages, which along with Indian languages, form the Indo-Iranian branch of languages. Modern Persian is the latest development of a language which has had several other periods of development, including Old Persian and Middle Persian. Old Persian is found in the inscriptions of the ancient family of Persian kings known as the Achaemenid family (about 550-300 B.C.), whose best-known members include Darius I and Xerxes I, both of whom controlled vast empires. Middle Persian was a continuation of Old Persian, but its grammar was simpler and its written form was a script adopted from Aramaic. Middle Persian literature includes writings of the religions of Zoroastrianism and Manichaeanism, as well as works of history, government, and ethics. Many of these works have been translated into Arabic and have enriched Arabic literature. Middle Persian evolved into Modern Persian, which has been the official and cultural language of Persian people (Iranians) for the past 13 centuries, since the Arab (Moslem) conquest in the 7th century. It is written in an enlarged Arabic script and includes Arabic words.

LESSON 5

Review your word list and take your final test. Write the words in the spaces provided at the back of this book. Begin with prayer and thank God for His help at the end.

UNIT 13

squaw	canoe	tepee	hominy
maize	raccoon	coyote	opossum
moose	papoose	wampum	tapioca
skunk	wigwam	quinine	moccasin
squash	hammock	tobacco	tomahawk

LESSON 1

Study the list words above, using the study plan on page 6.

LESSON 2

Use these list words in sentences.

canoe	moccasin	squaw
tobacco	coyote	tapioca

_____

_____

_____

_____

_____

_____

_____

_____

_____

_____

_____

_____

_____

_____

_____

_____

_____

_____

LESSON 3

Watch Your Language!

 Write the appropriate list words in the blanks.

Dwellings _____

_____

Animals _____

_____

_____

_____

Foods _____

_____

_____

_____

Weapon _____

Footwear _____

People _____

_____

Mineral powder _____

Watercraft _____

Hanging bed _____

Beads _____

Plant for smoking _____

 Label the following pictures with list words.

_____   _____   _____   _____

_____   _____   _____   _____

LESSON 4

Our Living Language

Write each of your list words three times on a separate sheet of paper. Review your word list and take a practice test.

Study the language history below and be prepared to summarize it from memory.

America is the region of the world which has the greatest variety of native languages, with an unparalleled number of tongues not understandable one to another. Hundreds of distinct Indian languages and thousands of dialects are spoken. Many of the languages are spoken by only a few dozen or few hundred people. Others are spoken or have been spoken by millions. The Indian-speaking population of the United States is currently quite small, the most widely spoken Indian language being that of the Navajo Indians in the Southwestern United States.

Although the American Indian languages greatly differ in grammar from those of the Indo-European langages, the Indian languages are difficult to classify as a group. However, all of them share, to some extent, one common characteristic: they all tend to have long words which take a number of words or whole sentences to express the same idea in English. The single Cherokee word *nod-hol-i-nin*, for example, means "bring us the boat" in English. Some of the Indian languages consist of a variety of standard syllables which can be combined in many different ways to create different words. These standard syllables can be shifted from word to word without changing their forms. Such languages are not made up of separate, distinct words that may be arranged in different ways to create sentences expressing different ideas, as in English.

The sound of Indian languages also differs greatly from one language to another and from European languages. Each has a particular sound, and each usually sounds strange to non-Indian ears. Pitch and tone are often important to expressing the correct idea, as in Chinese. For the most part, Indian languages follow strict rules and are far more complicated than European languages. Most Indian languages are not considered 'literary' languages; that is, there is no significant body of literature written in the Indian tongues. Ideas which other people express and preserve through literature are carried on through oral traditions by Indians. Yet most Indian languages are able to express extremely intricate thoughts and philosophical ideas. Some scientists believe that Amercan Indian languages evolved from a single, common language dating back to the earliest history of mankind. Others believe each language arose separately in the Americas.

Write these list words in the boxes. Find them in a dictionary. Write their meanings.

maize

quinine

hominy

tapioca

LESSON 5

Review your word list and take your final test. Write the words in the spaces provided at the back of this book. Begin with prayer and thank God for His help after your test.

UNIT 14

Words in regular type below have Asiatic roots. Words in slanted type have African roots.

gong	bamboo	bungalow	*giraffe*
junk	typhoon	madras	*satchel*
silk	muslin	macrame	*oasis*
mango	calico	*zebra*	*paper*
rattan	cashmere	*barb*	*gypsy*

LESSON 1

Study the list words above, using the study plan on page 6.

LESSON 2

Use these list words in sentences.

bungalow	**paper**	**cashmere**
typhoon	**satchel**	**oasis**

_____

_____

_____

_____

_____

_____

_____

_____

_____

_____

_____

_____

_____

_____

_____

_____

_____

LESSON 3

Watch Your Language!

1 Write these two list words. Find them in a dictionary or encyclopedia and write some information in the boxes about the plants they name.

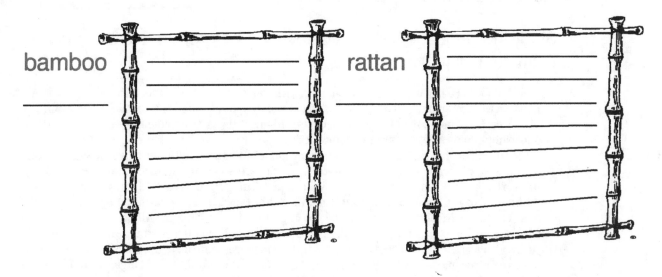

bamboo

rattan

2 Write these list words on the dark lines. Find them in a dictionary. Write brief definitions.

silk

muslin

calico

madras

cashmere

macrame

LESSON 4

. . . .

Our Living Language

 Write each of your list words three times on a separate sheet of paper. Review your word list and take a practice test.

 Study the language histories below and be prepared to summarize them from memory.

> More than 1,000 languages are spoken on the African continent. The most widely spoken is Arabic, which we have studied earlier. The next most widely spoken languages in Africa are Swahili and Hausa, each with more than 10 million speakers. Many of the African languages are spoken by only a few hundred or a few thousand people.
>
> The languages of Africa have been grouped by modern linguists into four language families: Afro-Asiatic, Nilo-Saharan, Khoisan, and Niger-Kordofanian. Some of the African tongues are believed to have had their origins more than 5,000 years ago. Writing systems exist for only about half of the African languages. For many people, the only literature they have in their own language is a Bible or New Testament. Missionaries have played the largest role in developing written languages in Africa. Missionaries, more than any other outside group, have also been interested in learning to speak African languages. The alphabets of most African languages were developed by Christian missionaries and are adapted from the Roman alphabet. Arabic and certain tribal languages of Ethiopia, Liberia, and Cameroon have their own writing systems.

> Asia, the world's largest continent, includes a vast number of peoples, cultures, and languages. The languages of this massive area of the world range from complex European-style tongues to simplistic languages such as Chinese. The main branches of language spoken in Asia include: Indo-European (Baltic, Indic, Iranian, Slavic, etc.), Altaic (Bulgaric, Turkic, Mongolian, Tungusic, etc.), Austro-Asiatic (Mon-Khmer, Munda, Annamese-Muong, etc.), Caucasian (Abkhazo-Adyghein, Daghestani, Veinakh, Kartvelian, etc.) Dravidian, Paleoasiatic, Malayo-Polynesian, Sino-Tibetan (Chinese, Thai, Tibetan, Burman, etc.). Each of these branches and families have many divisions. Space does not allow us here to discuss details of these many languages. One of the most important is Chinese, both because of its role in the long history and culture of the Chinese people and because it is spoken by so many millions of people. "Chinese" is actually a term signifying a number of closely related languages, including Mandarin, Hsiang, Wu, Foochow, Cantonese, and others. All Chinese-style languages are extremely simple in grammatical structure and limited in vocabulary. There are fewer than 500 different syllables, so voice tones are used to communicate meanings.

 Write African-based list words in the blanks.

AFRICAN SAFARI

If you went on a safari in Africa, you would likely want to see wild animals, such as a

_____ and a _____.

You might pack your gear in a _____ and take notes on a piece of _____.

If your trek took you into the desert, you might hope to refresh yourself and stay overnight at an _____.

LESSON 5

Review your word list and take your final test. Write the words in the spaces provided at the back of this book. Begin your test with prayer. Remember also to give thanks.

48

UNIT 15

Words in regular type below have Spanish roots. Words in slanted type have French roots.

ranch	corral	bonanza	*cache*
lasso	stampede	mosquito	*bureau*
plaza	mustang	alligator	*prairie*
bronco	adobe	pueblo	*gopher*
canyon	savanna	*levee*	*bayou*

LESSON 1

Study the list words above, using the study plan on page 6.

LESSON 2

Use these list words in sentences.

bureau	bonanza	cache
prairie	plaza	canyon

_____

_____

_____

_____

_____

_____

_____

_____

_____

_____

_____

_____

_____

_____

_____

_____

_____

_____

LESSON 3

Watch Your Language!

1 Write the list words derived from these Spanish or Mexican words.

_____ *rancho (camp, farm)*
_____ *estampida (loud noise)*
_____ *zavana (treeless plain)*
_____ *pueblo (people)*
_____ *plaza (broad street)*
_____ *lazo (noose, snare)*
_____ *bronco (rough, wild)*
_____ *cañon (narrow valley)*
_____ *corral (livestock pen)*
_____ *mesteño (stray animal)*
_____ *adobe (clay brick)*
_____ *bonanza (prosperity)*
_____ *moscita (little fly)*
_____ *el lagarto (the lizard)*

> An **Americanism** is a word that is characteristic of American English (as opposed to British English) and that entered the English language in America, even though its origins may have been in another language.

2 Write the list words derived from these French words.

_____ *levée (the action of rising), from 'lever' (to raise, to rise from bed)*

_____ *cache (hiding place), from 'cacher' (to hide)*

_____ *bureau (office, desk, cloth covering for desks or tables)*

_____ *prairie, from Old French 'praerie,' (meadow)*

_____ *gauffre (honeycomb)*

_____ *bayou, Louisiana French word from Choctaw Indian 'bayuk' (slowly moving creek, secondary watercourse, any body of water)*

> The American-English word 'gopher' is the common name for any of three burrowing animals: the pocket gopher, gopher tortoise, and pocket squirrel. Although unrelated, they all burrow in the soil and thus 'honeycomb' (French: gauffre) the soil.

50

Our Living Language

 Write each of your list words three times on a separate sheet of paper. Review your word list and take a practice test.

 Write these pairs of list words along with brief dictionary definitions.

prairie _____
_____
_____
_____
_____

savanna _____
_____
_____
_____
_____

bronco _____
_____
_____
_____
_____

mustang _____
_____
_____
_____
_____

ranch _____
_____
_____
_____
_____

pueblo _____
_____
_____
_____
_____

corral _____
_____
_____
_____
_____

lasso _____
_____
_____
_____
_____

LESSON 5
Review your word list and take your final test. Write the words in the spaces at the back of this book. Have you studied faithfully? Pray for God's help on your test, and He will bless you.

U*NIT 16*

ambient	contingent	itinerant	dissonant
complacent	imminent	incoherent	dissident
component	immanent	improvident	diffident
resonant	eminent	vehement	omniscient
insurgent	emanant	belligerent	elegant

LESSON 1

Study the list words above, using the study plan on page 6.

LESSON 2

Use these list words in sentences.

ambient	belligerent	omniscient
contingent	elegant	vehement

_____

_____

_____

_____

_____

_____

_____

_____

_____

_____

_____

_____

_____

_____

_____

_____

_____

_____

Watch Your Language!

1 Write these list words and match them to their meanings by writing the letter of the correct definition in the boxes.

_____ ☐ immanent

_____ ☐ imminent

_____ ☐ emanant

_____ ☐ eminent

A conspicuous, noteworthy, lofty, evident, outstanding

B flowing forth, emerging from, issuing as if from a source

C indwelling, remaining or operating within

D impending, ready to take place, near at hand

2 Write these list words and match them to their meanings by writing the letter of the correct definition in the boxes.

_____ ☐ dissonant

_____ ☐ dissident

_____ ☐ diffident

A not agreeing, not concurring, dissenting

B distrustful, doubtful, timid, lacking confidence

C marked by discord, unharmonious

3 Write these list words and match them to their meanings by writing the letter of the correct definition in the boxes.

_____ ☐ belligerent

_____ ☐ insurgent

_____ ☐ vehement

A warlike, inclined to hostility, combative, quarrelsome

B intense, severe, violent, emphatic, pronounced

C insubordinate, rebellious, in opposition to authority

4 Write these list words and match them to their meanings by writing the letter of the correct definition in the boxes.

_____ ☐ ambient

_____ ☐ contingent

_____ ☐ itinerant

A given to traveling from place to place

B associated with, dependent upon; by chance

C surrounding, encompassing, enveloping

Our Living Language

 Write each of your list words three times on a separate sheet of paper. Review your word list and take a practice test.

 Review the information in the heading for Exercise 1 on page 26. Write your current list words in the appropriate columns below.

-ent

-ant

_____

_____

_____

_____

_____

_____

_____

 The list words below are adjectives. They may also be used as nouns. Write two sentences for each word, using them first as adjectives and then as nouns. (You may use singular or plural forms for the nouns.) Write your sentences on a separate sheet of paper.

component   **belligerent**

itinerant   **insurgent**

dissident   **contingent**

The following '-ent' words name some of the attributes of God. Circle the list words. On a separate paper, write all the words and define them.

immanent
transcendent
omniscient
omnipotent
omnipresent

LESSON 5
Review your word list and take your final test. Write the words in the spaces at the back of this book. Have you studied faithfully? Pray for God's help on your test, and He will bless you.

UNIT 17

handicraft	stirrup	weevil	bladder
handiwork	gristle	mildew	bonfire
dwelling	mermaid	brimstone	shroud
holiness	yeoman	highland	barley
threshold	ankle	bramble	guest

LESSON 1

Study the list words above, using the study plan on page 6.

LESSON 2

Use these list words in sentences.

holiness	bonfire	threshold
guest	handiwork	shroud

_____

_____

_____

_____

_____

_____

_____

_____

_____

_____

_____

_____

_____

_____

_____

_____

_____

_____

LESSON 3
Watch Your Language!

1 Find the list words in these Bible passages (KJV). Write the list words in the blanks below.

I Timothy 6:13-16 _____

Psalm 47:8 _____

Psalm 19:1* _____

Revelation 21:8 _____

Luke 19:1-10 _____

* In some editions of the King James Version, 'handiwork' is spelled 'handywork.' In some newer editions, it is spelled 'handiwork.' Use the modern spelling here.

2 Rewrite these list words, correcting the spelling mistakes.

_____ blatter

_____ milldoo

_____ barely

_____ guessed

_____ handycraft

_____ holyness

_____ threshhold

_____ grissle

_____ mermade

_____ brambel

_____ handwork

_____ dweling

_____ stirup

_____ yohman

_____ ankel

_____ weavel

_____ brimeston

_____ hiland

_____ bondfire

_____ shrowd

3 Solve these word problems to form list words.

ye + omen - e + a = _____

stir + r + up = _____

we + evil = _____

mild + dew - d = _____

bone - e + fire = _____

guess - s + t = _____

handy - y + i + craft = _____

prank - pr + le = _____

br + amble = _____

bar + lee - e + y = _____

grist + le = _____

me + warm - wa + aid = _____

thigh - t + l + and = _____

bl + add +er = _____

sh + r + out - t + d = _____

holy - y + i + ness = _____

handy - y + i + work = _____

d + well + ing = _____

th + rush - u + e + old = _____

b + rim + st + one = _____

Our Living Language

 Write each of your list words three times on a separate sheet of paper. Review your word list and take a practice test.

Study the language history below and be prepared to summarize it from memory.

Anglo-Saxon is a name denoting the non-Celtic settlers of England. The term dates from the 16th century and refers to the German-speaking people who settled in England at the end of Roman rule. Angles probably came from Schleswig late in the 5th century. Saxons, another Germanic tribe, came to England about the same time and settled in other parts of the island. Jutes, another Germanic group, also settled in England and contributed to the development of the English language.

Anglo-Saxon is also the term used to describe the language that developed among these peoples during the period from about A.D. 449 to 1066 or 1100. This language has also become known as Old English. Old English consisted of four major dialects: Kentish, spoken by the Jutes; West Saxon, spoken by the Saxons, and Northumbrian and Mercian, spoken by the Angles. King Alfred of the West Saxons became the first king over all England in the 9th century, and with this the language of the West Saxons became the most influential in prose literature. However, a mixed Mercian dialect was used in poetry, most notably in the great epic poem, *Beowulf.* A few words of the conquered Celts entered Old English. A larger number of Latin words were brought into Old English, especially after Christianity spread into the British Isles.

Old English developed into Middle English, the term applied to the language and literature of England from about 1100 to about 1500. Norman invaders during this period contributed to the language.

In the late 15th and early 16th centuries, the transition from Middle English to Modern English began. A major change in this shift was in the way vowels were pronounced. This change in vowel pronunciation began to distinguish English from the other langauges of Western Europe. Modern English borrowed words from more than 50 different languages. The formal rules of Modern English grammar were established during the late 17th and early 18th centuries.

 Write the list words derived from these Old or Middle English words.

dwellen->_____

handiwerk->_____

handie-crafte->_____

halignes->holynesse->_____

threscwald->threshwold->_____

stigrap>stirop->_____

grost->gristil->_____

mermaide->_____

meledeaw->_____

scrud->_____

yong man->yoman->_____

ancleow->ankel->_____

brinston->_____

bonefyre->_____

bremel->brembel->_____

gaest->gest->_____

LESSON 5

Review your word list and take your final test. Write the words in the spaces at the back of this book. Always remember to begin and end with prayer. Prayer and study equals success.

UNIT 18

sauna	baffle	glimmer	squall
gnash	slaughter	smuggle	whine
greyhound	struggle	freckle	smorgasbord
luncheon	squander	dairy	kidnap
blunder	kidney	bulwark	whisk

LESSON 1

Study the list words above, using the study plan on page 6.

LESSON 2

Use these list words in sentences.

squander	dairy	freckle
struggle	whine	blunder

_____

_____

_____

_____

_____

_____

_____

_____

_____

_____

_____

_____

_____

_____

_____

_____

_____

_____

Watch Your Language!

1 Two of the words on your word list are taken directly, without alteration, from Scandinavian languages. Write the words below and learn their meanings.

smorgasbord

This word has been adopted directly from Swedish. It is a compound word, consisting of 'smörgås' (sandwich) and 'bord' (table). 'Smögås' itself is a compound word, consisting of 'smör' (butter) and 'gås' (goose). In English, the word has come to mean a lunch or supper buffet offering a wide variety of foods and dishes.

sauna

This word has been adopted directly from Finnish. It describes a type of bath developed in Finland. A 'sauna' bath is a bath of steam created by pouring or splashing water on heated rocks. After several minutes of such steaming, the bather then plunges into icy water. The word also refers to a bathhouse designed for such baths.

2 Most of the list words for this unit entered the English language during the periods of development of our langauge now known as Old English and Middle English (see language history on page 58). During these periods, Viking invaders from Scandinavia (especially Danes and Norsemen) infiuended English. Below are some of the old Scandinavian words which developed into modern English words. Study these old Scandinavian words and write the list words you think were derived from them. Other list words are of less certain origin.

Old Norse or Later Norwegian

Old Swedish

hvina (to whine) _____

kidh (child) + niupa (to pinch) _____

visk (wisp), viska (to wipe) _____

Old Danish

deigja (dairymaid) _____

glja (glitter) _____

smokelen (to creep), akin to Lower German (smuggeln) _____

bolr+verk (tree work) _____

slatr (butcher's meat) _____

Icelandic

skval (useless chatter, splash) _____

grey (female dog) + hund (hound) _____

frekna (freckle) _____

Our Living Language

 Write each of your list words three times on a separate sheet of paper. Review your word list and take a practice test.

2 Study the language history below and be prepared to summarize it from memory.

> The languages of Scandinavia include Norwegian, Swedish, Danish, Icelandic, and Finnish. The first four belong to various Scandinavian branches of the Germanic subfamily of the Indo-European languages. Finnish belongs to an entirely different subfamily known as the Finno-Ugric languages. Finnish bears no resemblence to the other languages of the Scandinavian region; however, many citizens of Finland do speak Swedish, one of the European Scandinavian languages. The Finno-Ugric subfamily includes Finnish, spoken in Finland; Estonian, spoken in Estonia; and Hungarian, spoken in Hungary; as well as several minor languages in northern Asia.
>
> Swedish, Norwegian, Danish, and Icelandic have many similarities. The kinship between Norwegian and Icelandic is especially close. All of these four languages appear to be derived from a common primitive Scandinavian language which can be traced through runic inscriptions to the 3rd century A.D. Some ancient "rune stones" may still be seen standing in the Scandinavian countryside where they have been for centuries. The Latin alphabet replaced the ancient rune signs when Christianity was introduced into the region. The four languages have influenced each other significantly, especially through literature and the spread of the Protestant Reformation in the Nordic countries.
>
> Viking conquerers invaded England during the Middle English period of language development there, and Scandinavian words, especially Danish and Old Norse, entered the English language. There is also a strong kinship between the Scandinavian languages and Old German, especially in vocabularies.

3 Write your list words in alphabetical order.

_____ _____ _____

_____ _____ _____

_____ _____ _____

_____ _____ _____

_____ _____ _____

LESSON 5

Review your word list and take your final test. Write the words in the spaces at the back of this book. Always remember to begin and end with prayer. Prayer and study equals success.

UNIT 19

picturesque	contour	clique	lozenge
millionaire	brunette	harass	jargon
privilege	moisture	bevel	jostle
harangue	nuisance	buttress	pique
entice	kerchief	garland	blouse

LESSON 1

Study the list words above, using the study plan on page 6.

LESSON 2

Use these list words in sentences.

| entice | harangue | harass |
| nuisance | jostle | contour |

LESSON 3
Watch Your Language!

1  **que = k** Write the four list words below. Circle the one that does not belong in the group.

picturesque _____

harangue _____

pique _____

clique _____

2 Write all list words with double consonants (two of the same consonants adjacent to each other). Circle the word with two sets of double consonants.

_____ _____

_____ _____

3 These sentences each contain a word which is also contained in one of your list words. Circle the word in the sentence and write the list word that contains it. (Do not consider the words 'a' or 'I.')

EXAMPLE: The truck (is) green. ___*moisture*___ (Do not use 'moisture' again in the exercise below.)

A. The artist painted beautiful pictures of the mountains. _____

B. My grandparents took a tour of Europe. _____

C. She was the fairest damsel in all the land. _____

D. Mother asked Father if he would open the jar of pickles. _____

E. She told you a million times never to throw your clothes upon the floor. _____

F. My uncle was the chief surgeon at our local hospital. _____

G. Jeff ran to the corner to catch the bus. _____

H. The air was badly polluted. _____

I. The two tennis players shook hands across the net. _____

J. A golden tress fell softly upon her shoulder. _____

K. "Thou shalt not covet thy neighbor's ox nor his ass nor anything that is thy neighbor's." _____

L. I would like a few ice cubes in my drink. _____

M. We went to church for our Christmas eve service. _____

N. Was that tiny bug a flea or a louse? _____

O. His car is running well now. _____

P. We are weak, but He is strong. _____

Our Living Language

 Write each of your list words three times on a separate sheet of paper. Review your word list and take a practice test.

 Write all the list words below whose meanings are uncertain to you. Find these words in a dictionary and write their meanings.

3 Write all the list words that are not written in the column at the left. Be prepared to tell their meanings if asked by your instructor.

LESSON 5   Review your word list and take your final test. Write the words in the spaces at the back of this book. Always remember to begin and end with prayer. Prayer plus study equals success.

UNIT 20

miniature	umbrella	regatta	granite
influenza	isolation	volcano	profile
manifest	domino	bravura	stucco
prima donna	fiasco	macaroni	stanza
malaria	fresco	spaghetti	studio

LESSON 1

Study the list words above, using the study plan on page 6.

LESSON 2

Use these list words in sentences.

fiasco	manifest	bravura
miniature	profile	isolation

LESSON 3

Watch Your Language!

1 Write the English list words derived from these Italian words.

_____ granito (grained, granulated)

_____ regata (Venetian gondola race)

_____ ombrella (parasol)

_____ miniatura (small-scale picture)

_____ manifestare (to declare)

_____ mala aira (bad air)

_____ maccarone (small cake)

_____ influenza (influence, epidemic)

_____ isolato (island)

_____ prima donna (first lady)

_____ vulcano (volcano)

_____ profilo (outline drawing)

_____ domino (lord, master)

_____ bravura (bravery)

_____ fiasco (bottle, flask)

_____ fresco (cool; fresh plaster)

_____ stucco (crust)

_____ studio (study)

_____ stanza (abode, room, stanza)

_____ spaghetto (little string)

2 Complete the following exercises.

A. Fill in the blanks to form two list words. ⟶ f __ __ **SCO**
f __ __ **SCO**

B. Write two list words that name diseases. ⟶ _____

_____

C. The word 'pasta' is another Italian word that has been incorporated into English. In Italian, it means 'dough' or 'paste.' We use the word 'pasta' to describe a variety of Italian-style food products made from a kind of dough. These become soft when cooked, and are often served with tomato sauces, cheese, ground meats, spices, and herbs.

Write two list words naming kinds of pasta.

_____

_____

65

LESSON 4

Our Living Language

 Write each of your list words three times on a separate sheet of paper. Review your word list and take a practice test.

 Review the history of the Latin language on page 13. Study the language history below and be prepared to summarize it when asked by your instructor.

3 Write all the list words below whose meanings are uncertain to you. Find these words in a dictionary and learn their meanings.

Write all the list words that are not written in the column at the left. Be prepared to tell their meanings if asked by your instructor.

Italian is the modern language that most closely resembles the ancient language of Latin. Italian is spoken in Italy, Sicily, Corsica, northern Sardinia, in the region along the northeastern shore of the Adriatic Sea, and in areas along the southern slopes of the Alps, including parts of Switzerland.

There are numerous, distinct dialects of Italian, all claiming to be the purest form of Italian. This fact has made it difficult to develop an accepted form of the language which would reflect cultural unity among Italian-speaking peoples throughout the Italian peninsula. Italian writers have tended, over the centuries, to write in their own dialects, and this has led to the creation of several different bodies of literature. Among these, books and documents written in the Tuscan dialect have tended to dominate, perhaps because of the central location of the province of Tuscany, its importance in commerce, and the fact that it is closest of all dialects to classic Latin.

Grammarians in the 15th and 16th century tried to make the pronunciation, syntax, and vocabulary of 14th century Tuscan the standard form of Italian. Their dictionaries have largely been accepted as the best authority on what constitutes Italian.

Modern Italian is considered quite easy to learn for people who have studied Latin or are familiar with any of its modern Romance forms. The simlicity of Italian phonics also makes it easy to learn.

Italian immigrants coming to English-speaking countries have contributed many words to English.

LESSON 5

Review your word list and take your final test. Write the words in the spaces at the back of this book. Always remember to begin and end with prayer. Prayer plus study equals success.

UNIT 21

cargo	tornado	commodore	siesta
negro	bravado	desperado	capsize
comrade	embargo	sombrero	armada
vanilla	dulcimer	guerrilla	guava
flotilla	hurricane	filibuster	cask

LESSON 1

Study the list words above, using the study plan on page 6.

LESSON 2

Use these list words in sentences.

embargo	capsize	filibuster
comrade	tornado	siesta

_____
_____
_____
_____
_____
_____
_____
_____
_____
_____
_____
_____
_____
_____
_____
_____
_____

LESSON 3
Watch Your Language!

1 Write these three pairs of list words. Find them in a dictionary and compare their meanings.

flotilla
_____

guerrilla
_____

hurricane
_____

armada
_____

desperado
_____

tornado
_____

2 Complete these list words.

_____illa   _____ado   _____argo

_____illa   _____ado   _____argo

_____illa   _____ado

3 Circle the word in each group that does not belong.

a. cargo
b. negro
c. embargo

a. bravado
b. tornado
c. armada

a. desperado
b. tornado
c. comrade

a. dulcimer
b. filibuster
c. sombrero

4 Write the list words derived from these roots.

Latin: *camera (chamber, room)*
Old Spanish: *cámara (chamber, room)*
Old Spanish: *camarada (group of soldiers sleeping in one room, roommate companion)*

Latin: *dulcis (sweet)*
Old Italian: *dolce (sweet)*
Spanish: *dulce (sweet)*
Middle French: *doulcemer >* **Middle English:** *dowcemere* *(sweet-sounding stringed instrument)*

English: *freebooter (pirate, pillager, one who goes about plundering for booty without authority of warfare)*
French: *fribustier (freebooter)*
Spanish: *filibustero (freebooter)*

Taino: *hura (wind, to blow away)*
Taino: *hurakán (strong tropical wind storm)*
Spanish: *huracán (strong tropical wind storm)*

Our Living Language

1 Write each of your list words three times on a separate sheet of paper. Review your word list and take a practice test.

2 Study the language history below and be prepared to summarize it when asked by your instructor.

3 Write some list words that have something to do with the sea or ships. (These may indicate something about Spain's history of seafaring and exploring.)

_____ _____

_____ _____

_____ _____

Spanish is one of the Latin-based or Romance languages, first spoken in the kingdom of Castile and therefore often called Castilian. It is now the official language of Spain, as well as much of the New World. The language was taken by Spanish explorers and colonists to Mexico, most of South America, the Canary Islands, the Antilles, the Phillippines, Central America, portions of the United States, and a few areas in Africa. Nearly 60 million people in the world speak Spanish, most of them in the Americas.

Latin is the base for Spanish vocabulary. A few words have come into Spanish from the Greeks, Celts, Basques, Germans, French, Italians, and Arabs. Spain's colonies in the Americas led to the introduction of a number of American Indian words as well.

Spanish is grammatically similar to French, Italian, Portuguese, and other Romance languages.

Most of the literature of Spain has been written in that form of the language known as Castilian since about the 11th century. During the 16th century, King Charles I of Spain inherited most of Europe and established many colonies in the New World. This period has become known as the golden age of Spanish literature, with the Dutch scholar and humanist Desiderius Erasmus influencing many of the Spanish thinkers and writers. Religious writings figure prominently in Spanish literature of the past, primarily due to the works of Roman Catholic monks and theologians.

4 Christopher Columbus was an Italian who sailed to the New World under a commission from King Ferdinand of Aragon and Queen Isabella of Castile. He sailed with a small fleet of three ships, the Niña. Pinta, and Santa Maria. Which list word best describes this small fleet?

_____

5 In 1588, King Philip II of Spain launched a large fleet of warships to do battle against England. The fleet included about 130 ships with some 30,000 men. English Captain Sir Francis Drake and other British commanders met the mighty Spanish fleet, forced it into the English Channel and soundly defeated the Spanish naval group. Only half of the fleet reached home. Which list word best describes this Spanish fleet of warships?

_____

LESSON 5

Review your word list and take your final test. Write the words in the spaces at the back of this book. Always remember to begin and end with prayer. Prayer plus study equals success.

UNIT 22

prior	radius	orator	translator
pastor	impetus	senator	alumnus
sponsor	nucleus	successor	animus
fungus	calculus	negotiator	squalor
genius	prospectus	investigator	census

LESSON 1

Study the list words above, using the study plan on page 6.

LESSON 2

Use these list words in sentences.

sponsor	successor	squalor
translator	genius	animus

LESSON 3

Watch Your Language!

1 Latin words ending in '-us' usually form their plurals by changing the '-us' to '-i.' This practice is retained in a number of English words that have been adopted unaltered from Latin. Among them are some of your list words. In some cases, both the old Latin form and the standard English plural form are acceptable. The dictionary will list the preferred spelling first. Below are all of your list words ending in '-us' and their various acceptable plural spellings. Write all of the words as shown and memorize the preferred (1st) and acceptable (2nd) plurals.

alumnus_____ > **alumni**_____

animus_____ > **animuses**_____

calculus_____ > **calculi**_____ > **calculuses**_____

census_____ > **censuses**_____

fungus_____ > **fungi**_____ > **funguses**_____

genius_____ > **geniuses**_____ > **genii**_____

impetus_____ > **impetuses**_____

nucleus_____ > **nuclei**_____ > **nucleuses**_____

prospectus_____ > **prospectuses**_____

radius_____ > **radii**_____ > **radiuses**_____

2 Write all your list words that end in '-or.' Circle the one that is an adjective.

_____ _____

_____ _____

_____ _____

_____ _____

Read Ephesians 4:11-12 (KJV). Which list word names someone who is one of God's gifts to His Church for its upbuilding?

_____

71

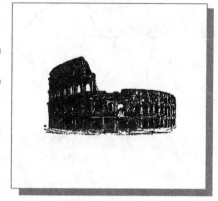

Our Living Language

 Write each of your list words three times on a separate sheet of paper. Review your word list and take a practice test.

 Circle the correct list word to fit the definition. Write the word in the blank.

A. A line from the center of a circle to the outside curve. _____	**animus** **radius** **nucleus**
B. A preliminary statement describing a forthcoming project or publication. _____	**prior** **prospectus** **sponsor**
C. A central point, part, or group about which other parts, mass, or activities take place. _____	**impetus** **radius** **nucleus**
D. Intention, governing spirit, effort toward an inevitable but not always recognized end. _____	**animus** **impetus** **genius**
E. One who has graduated from a particular school or college. _____	**successor** **genius** **alumnus**
F. A branch of mathematics involving calcuation or computation by use of symbols. _____	**census** **calculus** **fungus**
G. One who confers with another so as to arrive at a settlement of some matter. _____	**translator** **sponsor** **negotiator**
H. Dirtiness, moral baseness, corruption. the state or condition of filthiness. _____	**squalor** **fungus** **orator**

LESSON 5

Review your word list and take your final test. Write the words in the spaces at the back of this book. Always remember to begin and end with prayer. Prayer plus study equals success.

agitator	conservator	violator	intercessor
fabricator	interior	superior	malefactor
gladiator	inferior	moderator	liberator
educator	inquisitor	speculator	imitator
competitor	instigator	progenitor	procreator

LESSON 1

Study the list words above, using the study plan on page 6.

LESSON 2

Use these list words in sentences.

competitor	violator	liberator
instigator	intercessor	agitator

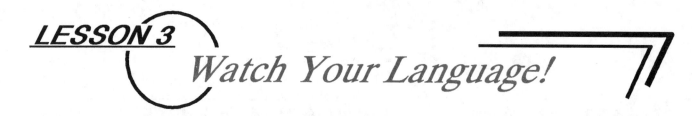

The noun suffix '-or' in Latin-based English words means:
1. one that does a specified thing (grantor = one that grants)
2. condition, activity (demeanor = one's conduct toward others)

Write list words naming 'one who . . .'

intercedes	_____
violates	_____
conserves	_____
agitates	_____
fabricates	_____
moderates	_____
liberates	_____
educates	_____
speculates	_____
imitates	_____
competes	_____
instigates	_____
procreates	_____
originates	_____
does wrong	_____
engages in combat	_____
inquires	_____

Three of your list words may be used as either nouns or adjectives. Write these three words.

inferior _____

adj. lower than

noun one who is beneath another

superior _____

adj. higher than

noun one who is above another

interior _____

adj. inside, situated in the center

noun something that is within

Write the two list words discussed on the lines below the explanations.

GLADIATORS

The word gladiator comes from 'gladius,' Latin for 'sword.' Literally it means 'one who fights with a sword.' In ancient Rome, gladiators were people who fought in a public arena. Some gladiators were professional fighters who engaged in public combat for sport and glory. Others were slaves, captives, criminals, or other condemned persons, who were forced to fight for the amusement of others. Many persecuted Christians were forced into the arena in this way. Thousands were killed by professional gladiators or wild beasts.

_____

INQUISITORS

The Latin word inquisitor means 'one who inquires, questions, or investigates.' When capitalized, the word refers to a member or official of the Inquisition. The medieval Inquisition began about A.D. 1233. It was a church court established to question and prosecute heretics (those who had departed from the established form of the Christian faith). The Spanish Inquisition (estab. 1478) was to spy out Jews and Moslems in Spain, but also later persecuted many faithful Protestant Christians. Some were tortured or put to death.

_____

LESSON 4

······················

Our Living Language

Write each of your list words three times on a separate sheet of paper. Review your word list and take a practice test.

Which list word best applies to the person described in the following paragraphs? Circle and write the correct word.

A. Shirley Laval has been practicing hard for the past 10 years in hopes of being named to the U. S. speed-skating team in the next Winter Olympic Games.	competitor conservator _____
B. The candidates for the City Council election plan to have a public debate. Charles Whitney, a local television commentator, has been chosen to be chairman and referee for the discussion.	inquisitor moderator _____
C. Leslie Louis has been a respected and effective science teacher for the past 15 years at Graybrook Christian High School.	educator inferior _____
D. Vladimir Lenin returned to Russia in 1905 to lead his followers in stirring up political, economic, atheistic, and social unrest in hopes of starting a revolution.	agitator procreator _____
E. When there is a fight among the children of the neighborhood, Mike Foley always seems to be the one who starts it or provokes others into fighting.	violator instigator _____
F. One of the criminals who was crucified with Jesus mocked the Savior and refused to repent of his evil-doing.	gladiator malefactor _____
G. Abraham is considered the ancestral father of the Jewish nation, and the Bible also describes him as the "father" of all believers because of his early faith in God's covenant promises.	progenitor superior _____
H. My grandmother, Abigail Berghuis, spent many hours of her long life praying for her children, grandchildren, missionaries, and other people in need.	imitator intercessor _____

LESSON 5 Review your word list and take your final test. Write the words in the spaces at the back of this book. Always remember to begin and end with prayer. Prayer plus study equals success.

UNIT 24

acme	caustic	epithet	monotony
tonic	phantom	ecstasy	enthusiasm
synod	exodus	phlegm	exhilarate
dogma	synopsis	paralysis	philanthropy
crisis	diadem	apology	dietary

LESSON 1

Study the list words above, using the study plan on page 6.

LESSON 2

Use these list words in sentences.

dietary	caustic	crisis
enthusiasm	monotony	synopsis

_____
_____
_____
_____
_____
_____
_____
_____
_____
_____
_____
_____
_____
_____
_____
_____
_____
_____
_____

LESSON 3

Watch Your Language!

1 Write the singular and plural forms of these three list words. Carefully study the change in spelling from singular to plural.

SINGULAR	crisis	synopsis	paralysis
	_____	_____	_____

PLURAL	crises	synopses	paralyses
	_____	_____	_____

2 Based on the pattern illustrated by the three list words above, write the plurals of these words of Greek origin.

thesis_____ a statement given for consideration or argument

synthesis_____ the combination of parts into a whole

antithesis_____ direct contrast, opposition, the direct opposite

parenthesis_____ a punctuation mark ( ) to enclose explanatory or qualifying remarks

hypothesis_____ a theory or assumption explaining a set of facts

analysis_____ separation of parts from the whole for study of the parts

ellipsis_____ omission of a word or phrase implied by context; the marks [. . .]

catharsis_____ the process of purging through release of hidden forces

catastasis_____ the dramatic climax of a play

prognosis_____ a prediction, especially about the course of a disease

hypnosis_____ an induced sleeplike state in which a subject accepts suggestions

metamorphosis_____ a transformation, a complete change

miosis_____ excessive contraction of the pupil of the eye

oasis_____ a fertile, watered area in the desert

psychosis_____ severe mental disorder involving withdrawal from reality

symbiosis_____ close, mutually beneficial relationship between two unlike organisms

3 Rewrite these sentences substituting a single list word for the words in parentheses.

1. The (church council) questioned the denomination's historic (body of doctrine).

_____

2. He hurled a (sharp or sarcastic) (term of abuse) at his enemies.

_____

Our Living Language

Write each of your list words three times on a separate sheet of paper. Review your word list and take a practice test.

Rewrite these sentences substituting a single list word for the word or words in parentheses.

1. He avoided milk because it seemed to produce (a thick mucus) in his throat.

2. The cereal box listed certain (nutrition-related) information on its side panel.

3. The dictator reached the (highest point) of his power after three years of ruling.

4. There was a certain amount of (sameness that produces boredom) to Christy's job.

5. Let me give you a (brief overview) of the (unstable state of affairs) we now face.

6. Taylor knew he was wrong and owed his sister an (expression of regret).

7. Casey always approached his work with a great deal of (fervor).

8. Marcia was in a state of (extreme rapture and exaltation) after winning the contest.

9. Andrew Carnegie was known for his (humanitarian generosity).

10. The bishop placed the royal (crown) upon the head of the new queen.

11. The phony doctor claimed his (liquid medicine) could cure muscle (loss of function).

LESSON 5

Review your word list and take your final test. Write the words in the spaces at the back of this book. Always remember to begin and end with prayer. Prayer plus study equals success.

UNIT 25

stigma	vigil	militia	sinister
consul	rostrum	panacea	arbiter
duplex	saliva	proviso	tribunal
murmur	diploma	genesis	nectar
veto	formula	interim	fulcrum

LESSON 1

Study the list words above, using the study plan on page 6.

LESSON 2

Use these list words in sentences.

sinister	formula	diploma
murmur	vigil	interim

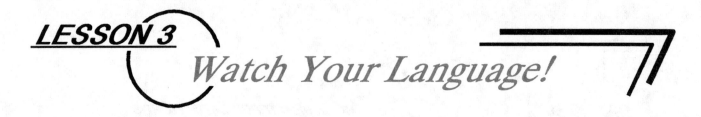

Watch Your Language!

1 Write the list words shown. Complete other list words in the 4 chains.

militia __ ☐ ___ ___ ___ ___

proviso ___ ___ ___ ___ ☐ ___

interim ___ ___ ___ ___ ☐ ___

panacea

2

Which two-syllable list word fits this diagram?

Syllable 1 ☐ ☐ ☐

Syllable 2 ☐ ☐ ☐

___ ___ ___ ___ ___

Our Living Language

 Write each of your list words three times on a separate sheet of paper. Review your word list and take a practice test.

 Rewrite these sentences substituting a single list word for the word or words in parentheses.

1. Rodney worked hard to overcome the (mark of disgrace) left by his criminal past.

_____

2. There is no (universal remedy) for our nation's moral problems, except repentance.

_____

3. Jill received a (certificate of completion) during her eighth-grade graduation service.

_____

4. The president promised to (reject and nullify) the bill approved by Congress.

_____

5. The governor called out the state (reserve armed force) to handle the emergency.

_____

6. The agreement included a (conditional clause) allowing future changes.

_____

7. The master of ceremonies approached the (raised platform for speakers).

_____

8. We took a short vacation during the (intervening period) between semesters.

_____

9. The family kept a steady (observing watch) at Grandma's bedside until she died.

_____

10. His so-called (outline of procedures) for success sounded (wicked and ominous).

_____

11. A (low muttering sound) arose when the (court of justice) announced its decision.

_____

LESSON 5   Review your word list and take your final test. Write the words in the spaces at the back of this book. Always remember to begin and end with prayer. Prayer plus study equals success.

UNIT 26

pall	placid	coerce	delirium
jilt	pallid	tenacious	fidelity
dirge	alien	gesture	alternative
farce	abscond	fragment	sacrament
rabid	adapt	replenish	vaccinate

LESSON 1

Study the list words above, using the study plan on page 6.

LESSON 2

Use these list words in sentences.

abscond	gesture	pall
coerce	replenish	farce

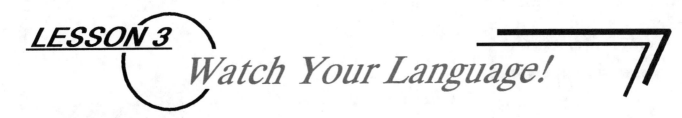
Watch Your Language!

 Solve this word problem by writing the suggested list words.

pall _____ + id _____ - all + lac _____ - plac + rab _____

2

t	e	n
a	c	i
o	u	s

How many words of two or more letters can you spell using these nine letters? Plurals OK. Do not use any letter twice in one word. Do not write proper names.

HOW TO SCORE: 2 points for every 2-letter word, 3 points for every 3-letter word, 4 points for every 4-letter word, etc.

TOTAL SCORE

LESSON 4

· ·

Our Living Language

1 Write each of your list words three times on a separate sheet of paper. Review your word list and take a practice test.

2 Write all list words in which the letter 'c' spells the sound of 's' as in 'sing.'

_____

_____

_____

_____

Write all list words in which the letter 'c' spells the sound of 'k' as in 'king.'

_____

_____

_____

_____

Write a list word in which the letter 'c' has the sound of 'sh.' ⟶ _____

3 Write the list word that contains the 'hard' sound of 'g' as in 'go.'

_____

Write all list words which contain letters having the sound of 'j.'

_____

_____

_____

_____

4 Write list words that are synonyms for the words below.

_____ mockery	_____ calm
_____ cloak; coffin	_____ foreign
_____ option	_____ escape
_____ secure	_____ force
_____ frenzied	_____ pale
_____ frenzy	_____ motion
_____ faithfulness	_____ particle
_____ accommodate	_____ holy observance

LESSON 5

Review your word list and take your final test. Write the words in the spaces at the back of this book. Always remember to begin and end with prayer. Prayer plus study equals success.

UNIT 27

supremacy	martyrdom	apprenticeship	matrimony
pilgrimage	abhorrence	brevity	lambkin
recital	transparency	solitude	rosette
forbearance	likelihood	foundling	rivulet
expectancy	barbarism	atonement	bullock

LESSON 1

Study the list words above, using the study plan on page 6.

LESSON 2

Use these list words in sentences.

solitude	forbearance	brevity
atonement	supremacy	likelihood

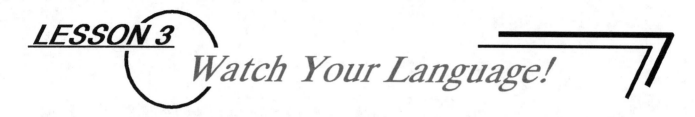

Watch Your Language!

 The suffixes used in your list words may be divided into two groups according to their meanings but come from various language sources. Study the suffix origins below and their meanings. Write the list words with each suffix.

State, quality, act of

_____	**-mony**	Middle English (-mony, -moigne), Middle French (-moigne), Latin (-monium)
_____	**-ment**	Middle English and Middle French (-ment), Latin (-mentum), Greek (-ma)
_____	**-tude**	Middle French (-tude), Latin (-tudo, -tudin-)
_____	**-ity**	Middle English (-ite), Old French (-ité), Latin (-itas, -itat-)
_____	**-ship**	Middle English (-schipe), Old English (-scipe), Old Frisian (-skip)
_____	**-ism**	Middle English and Middle French (-isme), Latin (-isma), Greek (-ismos)
_____	**-hood**	Middle English (-hod, -hode), Old English (-had), Old Frisian/Swedish (-hed)
_____	**-ency**	Middle English and Old French (-encie), Latin (-entia)
_____	**-ence**	Middle English and Old French (-ence), Latin (-entia)
_____	**-ancy**	Latin (-antia)
_____	**-ance**	Middle English and Old French (-ance), Latin (-antia)
_____	**-dom**	Middle/Old English/Old Swedish (-dom), Old Norse (-domr) Old German (-tuom)
_____	**-al**	Middle English and Old French (-aille), Latin (-alia)
_____	**-age**	Middle English and Old French (-age), Latin (-aticum)
_____	**-acy**	Latin (-ia)

Diminutives (small forms)

_____	**-ling**	Middle/Old English (-ling), Old German (-lingun), Lithuanian (-lenkti)
_____	**-kin**	Middle English/Old Swedish (-kin), Mid. Dutch (-kin, -ken, -kijn), Old Germ. (-chin)
_____	**-ette**	Middle English/French (-ette), Old French (-ete)
_____	**-let**	Middle English (-let, -lette), Middle French (-elet), Old French (-el + -et)
_____	**-ock**	Middle English (-oc, -ok), Old English (-uc, -oc)

Spell list word nouns by adding one of the suffixes above to these adjectives, nouns, or verbs. Note any spelling change in the base words.

_____	**rose**	_____	**recite**	_____	**abhor**
_____	**likely**	_____	**pilgrim**	_____	**lamb**
_____	**bull**	_____	**apprentice**	_____	**martyr**
_____	**brief**	_____	**atone**	_____	**forbear**
_____	**river**	_____	**supreme**	_____	**expect**

Our Living Language

 Write each of your list words three times on a separate sheet of paper. Review your word list and take a practice test.

 Rewrite these sentences substituting a single list word for the word or words in parentheses.

1. Several childless couples hoped to adopt the (tiny, abandoned infant).

2. A (young bull) was sacrificed as an (redeeming payment) for sins.

3. Joan's parents were joined in holy (marriage) on June 24, 1970.

4. Jody practiced faithfully for her upcoming piano (public performance by a student).

5. Civilized people have an (strong loathing) for (anything contrary to good taste).

6. "Or despiseth thou the riches of his goodness and (patience)..." (Romans 2:4a, KJV).

7. My grandfather's prayers were never known for their (briefness).

8. After teaching the crowds, Jesus went aside for prayer and (aloneness, seclusion).

9. The children looked forward to Christmas with great (waiting anticipation).

10. The (probability) of gaining (superior position) in the battle was increasing daily.

11. They crossed a (small river) during the first day of their (sacred journey) to the shrine.

LESSON 5

Review your word list and take your final test. Write the words in the spaces at the back of this book. Remember to begin with prayer and end with thanksgiving for God's daily help.

UNIT 28

misapplication	compression	synthetic	selective
misconception	relapse	syndrome	sequence
overabundance	pervasive	ashore	antitoxin
semidetached	metabolic	outguess	anti-Semitic
annotation	amphibian	epicenter	eccentric

LESSON 1

Study the list words above, using the study plan on page 6.

LESSON 2

Use these list words in sentences.

relapse	eccentric	sequence
synthetic	misconception	annotation

1 Study the prefix origins below. Write the list words that have these prefixes. (ME=Middle English; OE=Old English; MF=Middle French; OF=Old French; OS=Old Swedish; ON=Old Norse; L=Latin; Gr=Greek; OG = Old German, Skt=Sanskrit)

_____ **mis-** ME/OE (mes-, mis-), MF (mes-), OG/Goth (missa-, missi-, mis-), OS/ON (mis-) = 'to miss'
_____

_____ **a-** ME/OE (a-, an, on) = 'on, in, at'

_____ **out-** ME (out [adverb]) = 'out'

_____ **ec-** MF (yco-), L (oeco-, oiko-), Gr (oik- oiko-, oikos [noun]) = 'house'

_____ **an-** ME/MF/L (ad-) = 'to, toward'

_____ **com-** ME/OF/L (com-) = 'with, together'

_____ **re-** ME/OF/L (re-, red-) = 'again, anew'

_____ **per-** L (per-) = 'throughout'

_____ **meta-** MF/L/Gr (meta-) = 'between, with, after'

_____ **syn-** ME (sin- syn-), OF/L /Gr (syn-) = 'with, at the same time, by means of'
_____

_____ **amphi-** L/Gr (amphi-, amph-) = 'around, on both sides'

_____ **over-** ME/OE (ofer [adv. & prep.], OG (ubari, ubar), ON (yfir), Goth (ufar) = 'over'

_____ **epi-** ME/MF/L/Gr (epi-) = 'on, upon, to'

_____ **semi-** ME/L (semi-), OE (sam-), OG (sami-), Gr (hemi-), Skt (sami-) = 'half of'

_____ **se-** L (se, sed [prep.]) = 'without, after'

_____ **anti-** ME/OF/L (anti-), Gr (anti [prep.]) = 'against'

2 Write: **anti-Semitic** _____

The letters "Semi" in this word are not related to the prefix defined in Exercise 1 above, spelled 'semi-.' What does 'Semitic' mean? (See the language history on page 43.) What does the prefix 'anti-' mean? Based on your understanding of these two word segments, write a definition of 'anti-Semitic.' Consult a dictionary to confirm your answer.

_____

_____

Our Living Language

Write each of your list words three times on a separate sheet of paper. Review your word list and take a practice test.

Rewrite these sentences substituting a single list word for the word or words in parentheses.

1. The (point on the earth's surface) of the earthquake was 5 miles west of Barstow.

_____

2. Howard Hughes was clearly one of the world's most (unconventional) billionaires.

_____

3. The doctor prescribed an (agent to neutralize poison) to counteract the snake bite.

_____

4. A frog is an (animal capable of living on land and in water).

_____

5. The child's weakness signified starvation (group of symptoms typical of a disease).

_____

6. John's view of Christians was a (mistaken idea) based on his father's hypocrisy.

_____

7. Immorality has become (thoroughly spread or entrenched) within our society.

_____

8. The fabric was woven from (non-natural) fibers.

_____

9. Her mother warned her to be more (discriminating, particular) in her choice of music.

_____

10. By the mid-1930's, Nazi propaganda had grown more (hostile toward the Jews).

_____

11. They listened with a (somewhat aloof or indifferent) attitude to his arguments.

_____

LESSON 5

Review your word list and take your final test. Write the words in the spaces at the back of this book. Remember to begin with prayer and end with thanksgiving for God's daily help.

UNIT 29

Greek		Latin		English
bishop	=	supervisor	=	overseer
apostle	=	missionary	=	forerunner
analogy	=	correspondence	=	likeness
amnesty	=	oblivion	=	forgetfulness
apathetic	=	insensible	=	unfeeling
amorphous	=	informal	=	shapeless
anomalous	=	irregular	=	lawless

LESSON 1

Study the list words above, using the study plan on page 6.

LESSON 2

Use these list words in sentences.

apathetic	apostle	anomalous
oblivion	supervisor	irregular

_____

_____

_____

_____

_____

_____

_____

_____

_____

_____

_____

_____

_____

_____

_____

_____

_____

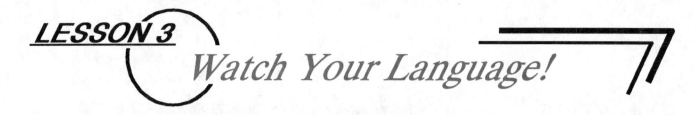

LESSON 3

Watch Your Language!

Examine the box on page 91 containing your list words for this unit. The words in the left column are derived from Greek. The words in the middle column are derived from Latin. The words in the right column are derived from early forms of English. The words are also arranged so that each horizontal line of words contains three synonyms, one word derived from each of the three languages. Write your list words in the table below, according to the example given.

	Greek	Latin	English
EXAMPLE ▶	*epistle*	*letter*	*writing*
	bishop		
			forerunner
		correspondence	
	amnesty		
			unfeeling
		informal	
			lawless

Write all your list words again below. In the boxes, write ⬜ A if the word is an adjective; write ⬜ N if it is a noun.

☐ _____   ☐ _____   ☐ _____

☐ _____   ☐ _____   ☐ _____

☐ _____   ☐ _____   ☐ _____

☐ _____   ☐ _____   ☐ _____

☐ _____   ☐ _____   ☐ _____

☐ _____   ☐ _____   ☐ _____

☐ _____   ☐ _____   ☐ _____

☐ _____   ☐ _____   ☐ _____

LESSON 4

Our Living Language

1 Write each of your list words three times on a separate sheet of paper. Review your word list and take a practice test.

2 The prefixes and suffixes below have negative meanings. Study the affixes and their meanings. Write G, L, or E in the boxes to indicate if they are Greek, Latin, or English affixes. Write the list words indicated.

a-, an-   *not, without*

☐ a- + pathos (feeling) + -icus (L., character of) _____

☐ a- + morphe (form) + -us (L., full of, having) _____

☐ an- + homalos (even, regular) _____

in-, ir-   *not*

☐ in- + sensire (to feel) + ibilis (capable of) _____

☐ in- + forma (form) + alis (of, characterized by) _____

☐ ir- + regula (rule, straightedge) + aris (of) _____

un-   *not*

☐ un- + felen (to feel) + -inge (of) _____

-less   *void of, lacking, without*

☐ shap (shape) + -les or -less _____

☐ lawe, lagu (law) + -les or -less _____

LESSON 5   Review your word list and take your final test. Write the words in the spaces at the back of this book. Remember to begin with prayer and end with thanksgiving for God's daily help.

93

UNIT 30

Latin / Greek			Anglo-Saxon / Greek		
satire	:	irony	chew	:	masticate
concise	:	laconic	dull	:	lethargic
student	:	scholar	star	:	asterisk
torment	:	tantalize	wind	:	meander
language	:	dialect	whale	:	cetacean

LESSON 1

Study the list words above, using the study plan on page 6.

LESSON 2

Use these list words in sentences.

meander	dialect	tantalize
lethargic	concise	satire

94

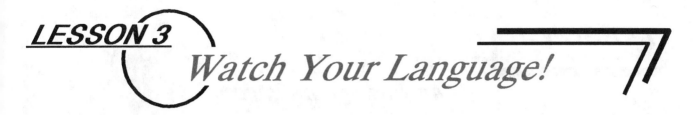
 Examine the box on page 94 containing your list words for this unit. Note that the second and fourth columns contain Greek-based words. The first and third columns contain synonyms of these Greek words derived from either Latin or Anglo-Saxon. Write list words in the table below. Examples (italics) are given, using words not on your word list.

Greek	Latin	Anglo-Saxon
energy	*vigor*	*strength*
		wit
		short
		learner
		tease
		speech
	xxx	chew
	xxx	dull
	xxx	star
	xxx	wind
	xxx	whale

Write all your list words again. In the boxes, write G, L, or AS to show if the word has been derived from Greek, Latin, or Anglo-Saxon.

☐ _____   ☐ _____   ☐ _____

☐ _____   ☐ _____   ☐ _____

☐ _____   ☐ _____   ☐ _____

☐ _____   ☐ _____   ☐ _____

☐ _____   ☐ _____   ☐ _____

☐ _____   ☐ _____   ☐ _____

☐ _____   ☐ _____

LESSON 4

Our Living Language

 1 Write each of your list words three times on a separate sheet of paper. Review your word list and take a practice test.

2 Unscramble these list words.

_____ **yonir**	_____ **kessatir**
_____ **whec**	_____ **thegarcil**
_____ **caneecat**	_____ **diwn**
_____ **telicda**	_____ **rats**
_____ **mertton**	_____ **dustten**
_____ **charsol**	_____ **zealtaint**
_____ **icenosc**	_____ **concali**
_____ **starie**	_____ **gluganae**
_____ **luld**	_____ **dreamen**
_____ **laweh**	_____ **catsmatie**

3 Write your list words in alphabetical order.

↓ _____	_____
_____	_____
_____	_____
_____	_____
_____	_____
_____	_____
_____	_____

Name these pictures with list words.

★ _____

✱ _____

_____

LESSON 5
Review your word list and take your final test. Write the words in the spaces at the back of this book. Remember to begin with prayer and end with thanksgiving for God's daily help.

UNIT 31

Anglo-Saxon / Latin		Anglo-Saxon / Latin	
saying	: adage	truthful	: veracious
hidden	: occult	eastern	: oriental
groundwork	: foundation	hatred	: repugnance
hurtful	: noxious	earthly	: terrestrial
enliven	: animate	swiftness	: celerity

LESSON 1

Study the list words above, using the study plan on page 6.

LESSON 2

Use these list words in sentences.

foundation	earthly	noxious
occult	oriental	adage

97

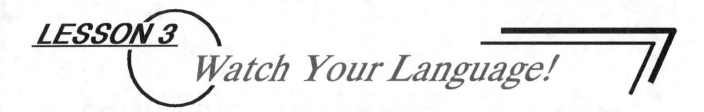

Watch Your Language!

1 Examine the box on page 97 containing your list words for this unit. Note that the second and fourth columns contain Latin-based words. The first and third columns contain synonyms of these Latin words derived from Anglo-Saxon. Write list words in the table below. Examples are given, using words that are not on your word list.

Latin	Anglo-Saxon
predict	*foretell*

2 Write all your list words again. In the boxes, write L or AS to show if the word has been derived from Latin or Anglo-Saxon.

☐ _____ ☐ _____ ☐ _____
☐ _____ ☐ _____ ☐ _____
☐ _____ ☐ _____ ☐ _____
☐ _____ ☐ _____ ☐ _____
☐ _____ ☐ _____ ☐ _____
☐ _____ ☐ _____ ☐ _____
☐ _____ ☐ _____

Our Living Language

■ ■ ■ ■ ■ ■ ■ ■ ■ ■ ■ ■ ■ ■ ■ ■ ■ ■ ■ ■

1 Write each of your list words three times on a separate sheet of paper. Review your word list and take a practice test.

2 Unscramble these list words. Arrange the letters in the boxes to write a familiar two-word adage in the large box below, right.

senstifsw _ _ ☐ _ _ _ _ _ _ _

stearen _ _ _ _ _ _ _

dinhed ☐ _ _ _ _ _

dorkgorwun _ _ _ _ _ _ _ _ _ ☐

ruthulf _ _ _ _ ☐ _ _

ruthulft ☐ _ _ _ _ _ _

veelinn _ _ ☐ _ _ _

clotcu _ _ _ _ _ _

nationfudo _ _ _ _ _ _ _ _ _ _

heartyl _ _ _ _ _ _ _

ginsya _ _ _ _ _ _

gaeda _ _ _ _ ☐

usoxoni ☐ _ _ _ _ _ _

temaina _ _ _ _ _ _ _

grupecanen _ _ _ _ _ _ _ _ _ _

thread _ _ _ _ _ _

trailrester _ _ _ _ _ _ _ _ _ _

cityreel _ _ _ _ _ _ _ ☐ _

rentalio ☐ _ _ _ _ _ _ _

creavusio _ _ _ _ _ _ _ _ ☐

3 Write your list words in alphabetical order.

↓ _____   _____

_____   _____

_____   _____

_____   _____

_____   _____

_____   _____

_____   _____

_____   _____

Collect boxed letters in order here. Unscramble in blanks below.

= _ = _ _ _ = _

ADAGE:

" = = = =

_ _ _ _ _ _ _ "

Write: **adage**

_____

LESSON 5
Review your word list and take your final test. Write the words in the spaces at the back of this book. Remember to begin with prayer and end with thanksgiving for God's daily help.

UNIT 32

stratum	paternal	federal	dual
custody	chord	docile	plume
tenuity	perforate	petition	flail
culminate	edible	fragile	cholera
farina	capital	torrid	circus

LESSON 1

Study the list words above, using the study plan on page 6.

LESSON 2

Use these list words in sentences.

culminate	docile	dual
custody	fragile	petition

_____

_____

_____

_____

_____

_____

_____

_____

_____

_____

_____

_____

_____

_____

_____

_____

_____

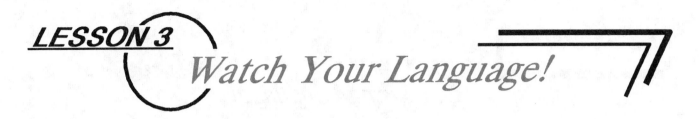
Watch Your Language!

Each of your list words for this unit has a Latin and Greek root. In the table below, the words in the left column are derived from Anglo-Saxon words that have a Greek/Latin root in common with one of your list words. Notice that the words have some relationship in meaning. Write all the words in the table below and learn their spellings.

Latin/Greek/Anglo-Saxon Roots	Latin/Greek Roots
straw	stratum
hide	custody
thin	tenuity
hill	culminate
barley	farina
father	paternal
yarn	chord
bore	perforate
eat	edible
head	capital
band	federal
teach	docile
find	petition
break	fragile
thirst	torrid
two	dual
fly	plume
blow	flail
gall	cholera
ring	circus

Our Living Language

 Write each of your list words three times on a separate sheet of paper. Review your word list and take a practice test.

2 Use these list words in sentences.

stratum	perforate	plume	(You may use the
tenuity	edible	flail	singular or plural
farina	capital	cholera	form of nouns and
paternal	federal	circus	verbs and any
chord	torrid		tense of verbs.)

LESSON 5

Review your word list and take your final test. Write the words in the spaces at the back of this book. Remember to begin with prayer and end with thanksgiving for God's daily help.

UNIT 33

warrant	truant	miraculous	rarities
potentates	muse	congealed	scythe
entangles	suffice	device	redemption
invention	haughty	alter	forfeit
throes	triumph	flourish	perpetual

LESSON 1

Study the list words above, using the study plan on page 6.

LESSON 2

Use these list words in sentences.

invention	miraculous	throes
haughty	redemption	forfeit

Watch Your Language!

1 Circle the list words you find in these excerpts of early English poetry. Write the words in the blanks.

Go, Soul, the body's guest,
Upon a thankless arrant:
Fear not to touch the best;
The truth shall be thy warrant....

Tell potentates, they live
Acting by others' action;
Not loved unless they give,
Not strong but by a faction....

Tell wit how much it wrangles
In tickle points of niceness;
Tell wisdom she entangles
Herself in over-wiseness....

From "The Lie" by Sir Walter Raleigh (1552-1618)

_____

_____

_____

Time doth transfix the flourish set on youth
And delves the parallels in beauty's brow,
Feeds on the rarities of nature's truth,
And nothing stands but for his scythe to mow:
And yet to times in hope my verse shall stand,
Praising thy worth, despite his cruel hand.

From "Likes as the Waves" by William Shakespeare (1564-1616)

_____

_____

_____

This is the month, and this the happy morn
Wherein the Son of Heaven's Eternal King
Of wedded maid and virgin mother born,
Our great redemption from above did bring;
For so the holy sages once did sing
That He our deadly forfeit should release,
And with His Father work us a perpetual peace.

*From "Ode on the Morning of Christ's Nativity"
by John Milton (1608-1674)*

Invention, nature's child, fled step-dame Study's blows,
And others' feet still seemed but strangers in my way.
Thus, great with child to speak, and helpless in my throes,
Biting my truant pen, beating myself for spite,
Fool, said my muse to me, look in thy heart and write.

From "Loving in Truth" by Sir Philip Sidney (1554-1586)

_____

_____

_____

Content to live, this is my stay;
I seek no more than may suffice
I press to bear no haughty sway;
Look, what I lack my mind supplies:
Lo, thus I triumph like a king,
Content with that my mind doth bring.

From "My Mind to Me a Kingdom Is" by Sir Edward Dyer (1550?-1607)

_____

_____

_____

What more miraculous thing may be told,
That fire, which all things melts, should harden ice,
And ice, which is congealed with senseless cold,
Should kindle fire by wonderful device?
Such is the power of love in gentle mind,
That it can alter all the course of kind.

From "My Love is Like to Ice" by Edmund Spenser (1552-1599)

_____

_____

_____

LESSON 4

Our Living Language

1 Write each of your list words three times on a separate sheet of paper. Review your word list and take a practice test.

2 The following song was written in Old English by an anonymous author. Rewrite it into modern English. Refer to the key for translations of the most unfamiliar words. You may rearrange and add words to make the song conform to modern English usage and structure.

KEY
awè: ewe
bleteth: bleats
buckè: buck
bulluc: young bull
calvè: calf
cu: cow
cuccu: cuckoo
icumen: come
lhouth: lows
lhudè: loud
lomb: lamb
med: mead (meadow)
murie: merry
naver: never
ne: not
nu: now
sed: seed
singès: sings
sterteth: leaps
swik: stop
thu: thou (you)
verteth: seeks cover
wel: well
wudè: wood, woods

Summer is icumen in, _____

Lhudè sing cuccu; _____

Groweth sed and bloweth med _____

And springeth the wudè nu. _____

Sing cuccu! _____

Awè bleteth after lomb, _____

Lhouth after calvè cu; _____

Bulluc sterteth, buckè verteth; _____

Murie sing cuccu. _____

Cuccu, cuccu, _____

Wel singès thu, cuccu, _____

Ne swik thu naver nu. _____

Sing cuccu nu! Sing cuccu! _____

Sing cuccu! Sing cuccu nu! _____

3 Write: **muse** _____ (noun)

This list word is taken from The Muses, nine sister goddesses of Greek mythology who were regarded as presiding over learning and the creative arts, such as poetry and music. The word 'music' traces from the Middle English 'musik,' the Old French 'musique', the Latin 'musica,' and the Greek 'mousike,' which meant any form of art presided over by the Muses, especially music. The Muses were believed to inspire poets. This idea was often expressed during the Renaissance, when classical Greek ideas again became popular. (See the poem on page 104 by English Renaissance poet Sir Philip Sidney.)

LESSON 5 Review your word list and take your final test. Write the words in the spaces at the back of this book. Remember to begin with prayer and end with thanksgiving for God's daily help.

UNIT 34

desolation	magnificent	gratifications	substitutionary
crevices	galleries	sentiments	meditation
impetuosity	transparent	forgiveness	testimonies
innumerable	concentrates	revelation	ancients
accessible	volatile	propitiation	precepts

LESSON 1

Study the list words above, using the study plan on page 6.

LESSON 2

Use these list words in sentences.

accessible	volatile	concentrates
sentiments	meditation	innumerable

_____

_____

_____

_____

_____

_____

_____

_____

_____

_____

_____

_____

_____

_____

LESSON 3

Watch Your Language!

1 Circle the list words you find in these excerpts from English literature. Write the words in the blanks.

They looked round on every side, and hope gave way before the scene of desolation. Immense branches were shivered from the largest trees; small ones were entirely stripped of their leaves; the long grass was bowed to the earth; the waters were whirled in eddies out of the little rivulets; birds, leaving their nests to seek shelter in the crevices of the rocks, unable to stem the driving air, flapped their wings and fell upon the earth; the frightened animals of the plain, almost suffocated by the impetuosity of the wind, sought safety and found destruction; some of the largest trees were torn up by the roots; the sluices of the mountains were filled, and innumerable torrents rushed down the before empty gullies.

From "Description of a Storm," Benjamin Disraeli (1805-1881)

_____ _____

_____ _____

Could there be a sweeter word in any language than the word "forgiveness," when it sounds in a guilty sinner's ear, like the silver notes of jubilee to the captive Israelite? ... Jesus tells me that I may yet be clean. Forever blessed by the revelation of atoning love which not only tells me that pardon is possible, but that it is secured to all who rest in Jesus. I have believed in the appointed propitiation, even Jesus crucified, and therefore my sins are at this moment, and forever, forgiven by virture of His substitutionary pains and death.

From "Morning and Evening," Charles Haddon Spurgeon (1834-1892)

_____ _____

_____ _____

The Bible, besides being the inspired Word of God, is also a work of Hebrew and Greek literature. The King James Version of the Bible has, for centuries, been considered one of the greatest of all works of English literature. Its rich majestic style gives it an enduring quality and has made it beloved throughout many generations.

The fox and wild cat chose more accessible haunts. Yet, here came the persecuted Christians and worshiped God, whose hand hung over their head those magnificent pillars and arches, scooped out those galleries from the solid rock, and laid at their feet the calm water, in its transparent beauty, in which they could see themselves sitting, in reflected groups, with their Bibles in their hands.

From "The Baptism," John Wilson (1785-1854)

_____ _____

_____ _____

It is not true that the poet paints a life which does not exist. He only extracts and concentrates, as it were, life's ethereal essense, arrests and condenses its volatile fragrance, brings together its scattered beauties, and prolongs its more refined but evanescent joys; and in this he does well, for it is good to feel that life is not wholly usurped by cares for subsistence and physical gratifications, but admits, in measures which may be indefinitely enlarged, sentiments and delights worthy of a higher being.

From "The Poet," William Ellery Channing (1780-1842)

_____ _____

_____ _____

O how love I thy law! it is my meditation all the day.
   Thou through thy commandments hast made me wiser than mine enemies: for they are ever with me.
   I have more understanding than all my teachers: for thy testimonies are my meditation.
   I understand more than the ancients, because I keep thy precepts.
   I have refrained my feet from every evil way, that I might keep thy word.

Psalm 119:97-101, The King James Version of the Bible

_____ _____

_____ _____

Our Living Language

1 Write each of your list words three times on a separate sheet of paper. Review your word list and take a practice test.

2 All of your list words for this unit have been taken from works of English literature. The exercise below demonstrates how English literature has been enriched by words from various sources, especially Latin. Write the list words derived from the following:

_____ **praeceptum (L: gave rules, instructed)**

_____ **propiciacioun (ME: the act of paying for sin)**

_____ **volatus (L: flew)**

_____ **galarie (MF: a chapel or porch of a church)**

_____ **forgifnes (OE: the act of granting relief)**

_____ **ancien (ME/MF: ancient; from L: ante [before] + anus [year])**

_____ **crevace (MF; from OF: crever [to break])**

_____ **desolatus (L: abandoned, deserted)**

_____ **sentiment (F; from L: sentire [to feel])**

_____ **magnificus (L: noble, splendid)**

_____ **accessus (L: approached)**

_____ **innumerabilis (L: not able to be numbered)**

_____ **com + centrum (L: with + center)**

_____ **revelacioum (ME; from MF: revelation; from L: revelare [to unveil])**

_____ **testimonium (L: Decalogue [10 Commandments], from H: eduth [witness])**

_____ **transparere (L: to show through)**

_____ **medisthai (Gr: to be mindful; ON meta: to value)**

_____ **impetere (L: to attack)**

_____ **substituere (L: to put in place of)**

_____ **gratificare (L: to gratify)**

L = Latin
ME = Middle English
OE = Old English
F = French
MF = Middle French
OF = Old French
ON = Old Norse
H = Hebrew
Gr = Greek

LESSON 5

Review your word list and take your final test. Write the words in the spaces at the back of this book. Remember to begin with prayer and end with thanksgiving for God's daily help.

UNIT 35

WORDS FROM WORLD LITERATURE

epistle	complain	intelligence	aspire
generation	efficient	perplexity	acceptable
encounter	contemplation	devotion	virtue
tempestuous	superstition	idealism	temptations
inscrutable	incongruous	despair	barriers

LESSON 1

Study the list words above, using the study plan on page 6.

LESSON 2

Use these list words in sentences.

| complain | intelligence | efficient |
| despair | acceptable | virtue |

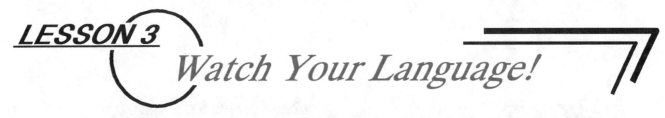

 Circle the list words you find in these excerpts from world literature. Write the words in the blanks. Discuss with your instructor whether the thoughts expressed are in keeping with Christian truth.

The world is God's epistle to mankind - His thoughts are flashing upon us from every direction.

Plato (427-347 B.C.)

_____

One generation passeth away, and another generation cometh; but the earth abideth for ever.

Book of Ecclesiastes

_____

The world is a great ocean, upon which we encounter more tempestuous storms than calms.

Edgar Allen Poe (1809-1849)

_____ _____

This world, after all our science and sciences, is still a miracle; wonderful, inscrutable, magical and more, to whosoever will think of it.

Thomas Carlyle (1795-1881)

_____

You and I must not complain if our plans break down if we have done our part. That probably means that the plans of One who knows more than we do have succeeded.

Edward E. Hale (1822-1909)

_____

The most efficient way to live reasonably is every morning to make a plan of one's day and every night to examine the results obtained.

Alexis Carrel (1873-1949)

_____

Prayer is the contemplation of the facts of life from the highest point of view.

Ralph Waldo Emerson (1803-1882)

_____

Superstition is ... religion which has grown incongruous with intelligence.

John Tyndale (1820-1893)

_____ _____ _____

Trouble and perplexity drive me to prayer, and prayer drives away perplexity and trouble.

Philip Melanchton (1497-1560)

_____

Devotion is love for something higher than ourselves; something that evokes our idealism; which while we despair becoming equal to it, yet makes us aspire to become like it.

The Kabbalah (1200 B.C. - A.D. 700)

_____ _____ _____ _____

The worship most acceptable to God comes from a thankful and cheerful heart.

Plutarch (A.D. 46-120)

_____

Prayer is a virtue that prevaileth against all temptations.

Bernard of Clairvaux (1090-1153)

_____ _____

Between the humble and contrite heart and the majesty of heaven there are no barriers; the only password is prayer.

Hosea Ballou (1771-1852)

_____

Our Living Language

Write each of your list words three times on a separate sheet of paper. Review your word list and take a practice test.

The quotations on page 110 from the Book of Ecclesiastes and St. Bernard of Clairvaux contain verbs with the Middle English verb suffix '-eth.' This suffix comes from the Old English '-eth, -ath,' and '-th.' It is used in verbs to indicate the third person, singular form of the verb. There are similar suffixes in Old Norse, Old High German, Goth, Latin, Greek, and Sanskrit. The Modern English form is '-es' or '-s.' Write the '-eth' verbs from the quotations on page 110 ending with '-eth.' Write the Modern English forms of these verbs.

Middle English	**Modern English**
_____	_____
_____	_____
_____	_____
_____	_____

Write the two list words below. Use the word parts in the boxes plus three other letters to form a third list word.

| temp | tations_____ _____ | incongr | uous |

_____ _____ _____

Write list words with these Latin-based prefixes: 'a-, ac-, com-, con-, de-, en-, in-, per-, super-.'

_____ _____ _____
_____ _____ _____
_____ _____ _____
_____ _____ _____

LESSON 5   Review your word list and take your final test. Write the words in the spaces at the back of this book. Remember to begin with prayer and end with thanksgiving for God's daily help.

UNIT 36

Review the words listed under each lesson and write them each twice on a separate sheet of paper. Prepare to be tested on some of them.

LESSON 1

abrogate	benevolent	docket	frequent	loiter	predestine	sherbet
abstinent	boor	drudgery	frolic	lubricate	pseudonym	skein
admonish	chemistry	elixir	griddle	masquerade	punctuate	slogan
algebra	chronicle	embellish	impertinent	mohair	quaff	supersede
anticipate	dialogue	enthusiastic	irreverent	morass	reconcile	symptom
assassin	discriminate	enumerate	knickknack	physician	relinquish	synonym
ballast	disparage	fascinate	knuckle	physiology	reprimand	yacht
beleaguer	dissonant	fluctuate	lackey	poignant	repugnant	yawl

LESSON 2

adamant	caravan	destination	heresy	invulnerable	moccasin	satchel
ambiguous	cashmere	dimension	hypocrisy	irrepressible	paradise	squash
amen	cherub	discourteous	illegible	jubilee	prototype	squaw
anonymous	cinnamon	fastidious	immutable	judicious	raccoon	tobacco
applicable	combustible	frivolous	impious	lethargy	rattan	tomahawk
architecture	compatible	gypsy	indignation	ludicrous	reminisce	typhoon
bachelor	contradiction	hallelujah	ineligible	macrame	rhapsody	velocity
bungalow	coyote	hammock	insidious	mango	sabbath	ventriloquist

LESSON 3

alligator	capsize	dissident	handicraft	lozenge	omniscient	spaghetti
ankle	clique	elegant	harangue	luncheon	plaza	squander
belligerent	commodore	embargo	harass	macaroni	prairie	stampede
blouse	complacent	fiasco	hurricane	mildew	profile	stirrup
bonfire	comrade	filibuster	incoherent	millionaire	regatta	threshold
bramble	contour	freckle	influenza	miniature	shroud	vanilla
bureau	corral	greyhound	insurgent	mosquito	slaughter	vehement
canyon	dairy	guerrilla	isolation	nuisance	smorgasbord	whisk

LESSON 4

abhorrence	apprenticeship	eccentric	inferior	nectar	rostrum	stigma
abscond	atonement	enthusiasm	instigator	negotiator	sacrament	superior
agitator	caustic	exhilarate	intercessor	nucleus	saliva	synod
alternative	census	expectancy	investigator	panacea	selective	synopsis
alumnus	coerce	formula	liberator	paralysis	sequence	synthetic
amphibian	competitor	genius	matrimony	placid	sinister	tenacious
annotation	crises	gesture	misconception	recital	solitude	transparency
apology	diploma	impetus	moderator	relapse	sponsor	vaccinate

LESSON 5

accessible	barriers	dialect	forfeit	meander	petition	tantalize
amnesty	chord	edible	foundation	miraculous	redemption	tempestuous
amorphous	concentrates	efficient	fragile	missionary	repugnance	temptations
animate	concise	enliven	haughty	oblivion	revelation	terrestrial
anomalous	correspondence	entangles	idealism	occult	scholar	testimonies
apathetic	culminate	epistle	language	oriental	sentiments	triumph
apostle	custody	federal	lethargic	perforate	substitutionary	veracious
asterisk	desolation	flourish	magnificent	perplexity	superstition	warrant

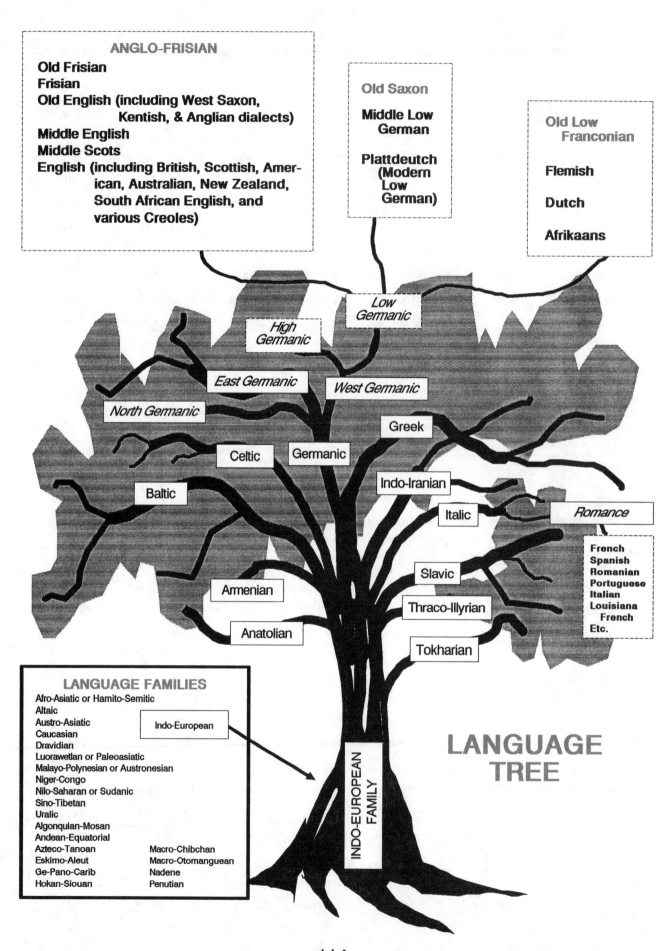

ANGLO-FRISIAN

Old Frisian
Frisian
Old English (including West Saxon,
       Kentish, & Anglian dialects)
Middle English
Middle Scots
English (including British, Scottish, American, Australian, New Zealand,
       South African English, and
       various Creoles)

Old Saxon

Middle Low German

Plattdeutch (Modern Low German)

Old Low Franconian

Flemish

Dutch

Afrikaans

Low Germanic

High Germanic

East Germanic

West Germanic

North Germanic

Greek

Celtic

Germanic

Indo-Iranian

Baltic

Italic

Romance

French
Spanish
Romanian
Portuguese
Italian
Louisiana French
Etc.

Armenian

Slavic

Thraco-Illyrian

Anatolian

Tokharian

LANGUAGE FAMILIES

Afro-Asiatic or Hamito-Semitic
Altaic
Austro-Asiatic
Caucasian
Dravidian
Luorawetlan or Paleoasiatic
Malayo-Polynesian or Austronesian
Niger-Congo
Nilo-Saharan or Sudanic
Sino-Tibetan
Uralic
Algonquian-Mosan
Andean-Equatorial
Azteco-Tanoan   Macro-Chibchan
Eskimo-Aleut   Macro-Otomanguean
Ge-Pano-Carib   Nadene
Hokan-Siouan   Penutian

Indo-European

INDO-EUROPEAN FAMILY

LANGUAGE TREE

UNIT 1 TEST

UNIT 2 TEST

UNIT 3 TEST

UNIT 4 TEST

UNIT 5 TEST

UNIT 6 TEST

UNIT 7 TEST	UNIT 8 TEST	UNIT 9 TEST

UNIT 10 TEST

UNIT 11 TEST

UNIT 12 TEST

UNIT 13 TEST	UNIT 14 TEST	UNIT 15 TEST

UNIT 16 TEST

UNIT 17 TEST

UNIT 18 TEST

UNIT 25 TEST

UNIT 26 TEST

UNIT 27 TEST

UNIT 28 TEST

_____

_____

_____

_____

_____

_____

_____

_____

_____

_____

_____

_____

_____

_____

_____

_____

_____

_____

UNIT 29 TEST

_____

_____

_____

_____

_____

_____

_____

_____

_____

_____

_____

_____

_____

_____

_____

_____

_____

_____

UNIT 30 TEST

_____

_____

_____

_____

_____

_____

_____

_____

_____

_____

_____

_____

_____

_____

_____

_____

_____

_____

UNIT 31 TEST

UNIT 32 TEST

UNIT 33 TEST

UNIT 34 TEST

UNIT 35 TEST

UNIT 36 TEST